Essentials of Tai Chi and Qigong

David-Dorian Ross, B.A.

THE
GREAT
COURSES®

PUBLISHED BY:

THE GREAT COURSES
Corporate Headquarters
4840 Westfields Boulevard, Suite 500
Chantilly, Virginia 20151-2299
Phone: 1-800-832-2412
Fax: 703-378-3819
www.thegreatcourses.com

David-Dorian Ross, B.A.
International Master Tai Chi Instructor

David-Dorian Ross is the founder and CEO of TaijiFit and the creator of the TaijiFit program, a revolution in mind-body exercise. He has a B.A. in Human Movement Studies from San Francisco State University, has completed graduate course work in Physical Education and Chinese, and is currently developing a project with the head of the Harvard Medical School research department to study the stress-reduction benefits of tai chi (taiji) in the workplace.

Mr. Ross has successfully sought to modernize and mainstream the teaching methods used to transmit the ancient mind-body disciplines to contemporary students without losing the essence of those arts. Since 2012, he has collaborated with international action film star Jet Li on a mission to introduce tai chi to 100 million new people worldwide by the year 2020.

Mr. Ross has been a fitness industry leader for more than 30 years. He was the founder and chief instructor of the Honolulu T'ai Chi Academy and a certified continuing educator for the American Council on Exercise. He is recognized as an expert on mind-body fitness in particular but also on fitness in general. He has been a presenter at virtually every major fitness conference in the United States, Canada, and China and has served as a committee member for several organizations, including the National Association of Health and Fitness.

Mr. Ross's competitive performances have won him seven U.S. gold medals, two world bronze medals, and a world silver medal—the highest awards ever given to an American for international tai chi performance. His tai chi training includes studying in China with the coach of the women's world tai chi champion and with Wu Bin, the former head coach of the Chinese national martial arts team. In the United States, Mr. Ross's teachers include

Grandmaster Doc-Fai Wong and Master Wen-Mei Yu, and for the past eight years, he has been the student of Master Wei Jingling.

Mr. Ross is the creator of a dozen award-winning DVDs, including *T'ai Chi Beginning Practice* (the number-one selling tai chi video in America), produced by Gaiam. He also hosted the PBS television special *T'ai Chi: Health and Happiness*. His first show on PBS was *T'ai Chi in Paradise*. He is the author of five books on health and wellness, including *Exercising the Soul*, an Amazon number-one best seller in the meditation category.

Mr. Ross's company, TaijiFit, aims to combine the best of traditional tai chi with modern Western fitness for health and happiness. His list of clients includes LinkedIn (on the corporate fitness side). In 2011, when LA Fitness bought Bally Total Fitness, Mr. Ross was hired to recertify more than 1,000 LA Fitness personal trainers.

Mr. Ross is a pioneer in the use of social media and the Internet to teach tai chi, qigong, and meditation. He created the first online full-service mind-body training studio at daviddorianross.com, with all classes at the studio held in real time via two-way video. The curriculum's centerpiece is the TaijiFit program, but it also includes yoga as well as Nia (neuromuscular integrative action) and classical tai chi (taijiquan). ∎

Disclaimer

This series of lectures is intended to convey general health, fitness, and nutritional information and is for educational purposes only. It is not a substitute for, nor does it replace, professional medical advice, diagnosis, or treatment of health conditions. Please consult your physician or other health-care professional before beginning or changing any fitness or nutrition program to make sure that it is appropriate for your needs.

If you have any concerns or questions about your health, you should always consult a physician or other health-care professional. Do not disregard, avoid, or delay obtaining medical or health-related advice from your health-care professional because of something you may have seen or heard in these lectures. Current health and fitness research may exist that could affect the educational information provided in these lectures, and advice found herein may not be based on the most recent findings or developments. Therefore, the use of any information provided in these lectures is solely at your own risk. By continuing with the programs, exercises, advice, information, or diets discussed in these lectures, you recognize that there are risks of injury or illness that can occur because of your use of the aforementioned information, and you expressly assume such risks and waive, relinquish, and release any claim that you may have against The Teaching Company as a result of any future physical injury or illness incurred in connection with, or as a result of, use or misuse of the programs, exercises, advice, diets, and/or information discussed in these lectures. The opinions and positions provided in these lectures reflect the opinions and positions of the relevant lecturer and do not necessarily reflect the opinions or positions of The Teaching Company or its affiliates.

The Teaching Company expressly DISCLAIMS LIABILITY for any DIRECT, INDIRECT, INCIDENTAL, SPECIAL, OR CONSEQUENTIAL DAMAGES OR LOST PROFITS that result directly or indirectly from the use of these lectures. In states that do not allow some or all of the above limitations of liability, liability shall be limited to the greatest extent allowed by law.

Table of Contents

Table of Contents

Table of Contents

Essentials of Tai Chi and Qigong

Scope:

This course is a guided exploration of the many facets of two ancient Chinese energetic arts. We call them "energetic" because at the heart of both practices is the belief in an intrinsic life energy known as qi, "spirit breath" or "life force." Tai chi chuan—perhaps the more well known of the two (at least in the West)—is a martial art based on very unique principles, including the emphasis on developing qi mastery. Qigong is the practice of developing greater awareness and control over the inner life energy for therapeutic and healing purposes.

Both tai chi chuan and qigong are related and for centuries have been practiced together—each discipline evolving its own set of exercises, yet each resembling each other greatly and even sharing a majority of each other's organizing principles. Recently, both practices have received renewed attention, because many respected research institutions, such as Harvard Medical School and the Mayo Clinic, have published articles touting the superior health benefits of tai chi and qigong.

This course will take you on a journey through the rich landscape of tai chi and qigong, covering the spectrum of topics from their early recorded history to how they are evolving in the 21st century. Each lecture also includes segments in which you will be led through simple yet energizing qigong exercises, as well as "easy tai chi" practices to get you into the flow. You will also learn an entire tai chi chuan routine, known as the 24-movement Yang short form, which is recognized as the most popular tai chi chuan routine in the world. Each of the 24 lectures includes a lesson on another movement in the routine—or "form"—so that by the end of the course, you will have learned the entire routine.

The course begins with an overview of some of the most essential features of tai chi chuan and qigong. Foremost among these is the philosophy of balance and harmony. In fact, a strict translation of the phrase "tai chi" is "supreme ultimate," which in Chinese means "balance and harmony." It is this philosophy that provides a continuous connecting theme throughout most of the topics covered in this course—from the use of weapons in tai chi to applying principles of tai chi in the business arena.

Various lectures in this course cover the health and fitness benefits of tai chi and qigong practice. These disciplines have long been praised by devotees and aficionados, but many in the scientific and medical communities have been skeptical of their actual health benefits. In this course, you will learn about the many research projects (numbering in the hundreds) that have studied tai chi's effects on almost every major disease. The results of every study show at least two undisputed claims: that tai chi and qigong have positive health effects on multiple levels and that there are no known side effects or contraindications associated with their use.

Two of the lectures in this course cover the medical benefits for a number of other health concerns in addition to heart disease. General fitness benefits are also explored in this course, helping to answer the question, "Can tai chi practice help me lose weight and build muscle?"

In addition to their health and fitness benefits, tai chi chuan and qigong are traditionally taught as self-cultivation or self-development practices. By embracing the philosophy of balance and harmony, you can learn to make every aspect of life happier, healthier, more compassionate, and more successful. In the final third of this course, you will explore how tai chi and qigong can be used to live a better life in the contemporary Western world. In one lecture, you will be introduced to a way of interpreting the traditional elements of tai chi into a language more applicable to corporate culture. Tai chi chuan and qigong have lessons that can improve a company's morale, creativity, teamwork, and, of course, bottom line.

This course offers a comprehensive overview of tai chi and qigong. It covers topics that are typically written about but also many aspects often only known to advanced students of these martial arts. The goal of this course is to capture your interest and imagination and to entice you to weave these practices into your lifestyle. ∎

The Snake and the Crane
Lecture 1

There is a saying in Chinese culture that knowing where you came from helps you to understand better where you are. And that is especially true with tai chi, where there is always more to learn. Throughout this course, you will be exploring various aspects of tai chi—along with its companion practice, qigong—in depth. Tai chi and qigong are often referred to as "treasures of Chinese culture"; studying them is like holding a beautiful jewel, where each time you turn, you see a new facet. Hopefully, tai chi will enchant and entice you and you'll be drawn to make tai chi practice part of your lifestyle.

The Story of Tai Chi

- A long time ago in medieval China (during the Yuan dynasty, some say, around 800 years ago), a legendary priest named Zhang Sanfeng had gone high into the Wudang mountains of north central China to study the philosophy of yin and yang with the monks at the Wudang temple.

- Their teaching spoke of a great mystery: that the entire universe was a dance of opposite but balancing forces. Understanding this mystery could lead one to an ultimate state of harmony, longevity, and inner peace.

- Early one morning, Zhang's meditation was disturbed by a loud sound coming from the courtyard below his window. When he looked outside, he discovered a snake and crane fighting with each other. As the crane pecked at the snake with its long, deadly beak, the snake coiled and twisted and evaded the attacks. And when the snake struck at the crane, the bird hopped and turned, balancing first on one leg and then the other. The snake could not catch the bird, no matter how he tried. And the crane's direct attacks were neutralized by the snake's circles and spirals. The fluid interplay of the two animals looked more like a dance than a deadly battle.

3

- Watching this scene, Zhang had an epiphany. The philosophy of yin and yang is not just an abstract idea—it is a principle of nature, and it can be seen everywhere. Straight lines are balanced by circles and coils; attacks are balanced by yielding and melting away. If Zhang could only mimic this kind of dance, he could teach it to others, and they could learn the secrets of balance and harmony.

- Working with the monks at Wudang, he developed a beautiful dance that was also a deadly martial art—a martial art whose fundamental principle is that softness will always overcome hardness, and harmonious mind and body will always win out over chaotic mind and body.

- We call this dance tai chi—more precisely, tai chi chuan, a mash-up of the Chinese expression for total balance, which is pronounced "tai chi" (that's where we get the more well-known phrase from), and the word *chuan*, which translates as "fist" but is understood to mean a martial arts discipline or style.

The Birth of Qigong

- Traditionally, tai chi is studied alongside another discipline, known as qigong, or "energy exercises." Nearly 2,000 years ago, a great flood ravaged China—and after the flood, a plague did the same. Concerned for the common people, a great physician named Hua Tuo traveled to the countryside to see if he could determine the cause of the epidemic.

- His discovery astonished him. "People," he later wrote, "are like water. Water that moves and flows freely is clean and healthy. But water that is stagnant breeds pestilence."

- After the flood, the peasants were homeless, with their farms destroyed and their crops and fields devastated. They sat around all day, and like stagnant water, they developed disease. Hua Tuo surmised that a lethargic body affected one's inner life source, an energy known in Chinese as "qi," the "spirit breath." Sluggish qi, like sluggish water, was responsible for the plague.

- But Hua Tuo discovered something else: None of the wild animals were sick—only the people. So, Hua Tuo invented a new kind of exercise called the *wu qin xi*, "the frolic of the five animals," a workout mimicking the motions of the tiger, the deer, the bear, the monkey, and the crane. It is the first recorded system of what is known as qigong.

- For the next 2,000 years, up to today, tai chi and qigong have traditionally been studied side by side as the ultimate workout for the body, mind, and spirit. Born in the mists of ancient China, both are now enjoyed by millions of people around the world for health, exercise, and even self-defense.

The Evolution of Tai Chi

- A lot of people are curious about how old tai chi is. Most historians trace what we call tai chi chuan to the Chen clan of Henan province, China, not far from where the Wudang mountains are located. In particular, tai chi historians focus on three particular names of the Chen family, who represent a step-by-step evolution toward the tai chi we know today.

- The first person we hear about is the first patriarch of the Chen family, Chen Bu, who emigrated in the late 1300s to Henan province from his family's original home in Shanxi province. His move was part of a national relocation program, when the new ruling dynasty came in.

- Chen Bu was a martial artist of some skill, apparently, and to protect his family and neighbors from the bandits who lived in the area, he taught them all some martial arts. This became known as Chen boxing, the earliest lineage of contemporary tai chi chuan. It was a style that featured—and still features—explosive release of energy known as *fa jing*.

- The Chen family flourished in the area so much that the new village became known as Chen's village.

- The second member of the Chen family to notice is the 9th-generation patriarch of the Chen family, Chen Wan-ting, who brought together all the previous Chen training practices. And he made some additional innovations. He also brought in elements of other boxing styles he had learned before—during his time as first an armed caravan escort and later as a general in the Ming army.

- He started a new practice method—a pre-sparring sensitivity practice—called *tui shou*, which means "pushing hands." He is credited with integrating yin-yang theory into the actual fighting techniques of Chen boxing. He brought in *dao yin* (leading and guiding energy) and *tu na* (expelling and drawing energy).

- All of these innovations sent Chen boxing into a new direction (in particular, with a focus on developing qi mastery) for several generations.

- The third member of the Chen family we remember comes in the 19th century, with the 14th-generation Chen patriarch, Chen Chang-xing, who consolidated the Chen routines into two forms, known as Chen I and II (it's now referred to as the "old format" I and II). This simplified the curriculum of study. In fact, all of the modern forms and styles trace their origins back to Chen Chang-xing's old format I.

- But the main reason we remember him is because he accepted as a student the first outsider of the Chen family: a boy named Yang Lu-chan, who would go on later in life to create his own new style of tai chi.

- Yang-style tai chi was born in the mid-19th century. This is a critical moment in the history of tai chi chuan, because now this art starts to become known and available outside of Chen village and the Chen family. Moreover, whereas the Chen style is especially challenging, even today, the Yang style features more of the large, slow movements often associated with tai chi in the popular mind.

- Yang Lu-chan's grandson, Yang Chen-fu, was a successful entrepreneur and promoter of tai chi. Perhaps more than anyone else, he is responsible for the preservation and popularity of modern tai chi. He traveled throughout China in the early 1920s and 1930s at the invitation of wealthy families and martial arts groups to teach his special family martial art.

- At the same time, he was also spreading a message that tai chi would help strengthen the people of the Chinese nation. He left behind hundreds of disciples, and many of them emigrated to other parts of Southeast Asia, Australia, and eventually the United States. Without this diaspora, tai chi would not be as well known around the world as it is today—and it might not have survived at all.

The Short Form
- One of the biggest events in recent times was the creation of the 24-movement simplified Yang family short form, commonly referred to as the "short form" or the "Beijing form." Choreographed in 1959 by China's national Physical Culture and Sports committee, this compact tai chi routine was part of China's first national fitness program.

- The most important thing about this form was that it was easy enough and short enough that it traveled well. It was taught primarily for health and exercise in China, but it has made its way into thousands of traditional tai chi chuan schools around the world.

- Now it is the most widely recognized and practiced tai chi chuan routine on the planet. The short form also made tai chi chuan more accessible to Westerners and non–martial artists. In fact, this is the form you will be learning across the 24 lectures of this series.

- The creation of the 24-movement form marked a shift in the predominant approach to tai chi chuan. Whereas previously it was primarily an activity for martial artists, now it was being seen as an activity open to everyone—and not one requiring that one do it to hone fighting skills.

The 24-movement Yang family short form of tai chi was taught primarily for health and exercise in China.

- In China, people began doing tai chi as their primary daily exercise or health therapy. They found it so beneficial that they began spreading stories that tai chi could cure disease and relieve chronic pain. Hospitals and universities began research to see if tai chi chuan and qigong were really as effective as tai chi enthusiasts claimed.

- These studies have finally caught up to the West. Respected institutions like the Mayo Clinic, Johns Hopkins University, and Harvard Medical School all published studies early in the 21st century reporting the amazing health and fitness benefits of tai chi practices.

Suggested Reading

Olson and Gross, *Tai Ji Quan Treatise*.

Sim and Gaffney, *Chen Style Taijiquan*.

1. Take 30 minutes to observe nature. Notice the wind in the trees, the birds flying, or the water in a stream. Watch for this pattern: When in action, the whole "body" is in motion. When not in action, the whole body is still.

2. In this lecture, you were introduced to your first simple qigong exercise: sinking the qi. Try adding just a few minutes of this every day—when you get out of bed in the morning, at lunchtime, and just before retiring at night. Start with just three repetitions each time.

First Steps in a Journey
Lecture 2

In this lecture, you will be starting on your journey into tai chi. Many people discover tai chi, and then it becomes a lifelong practice. Many students begin tai chi in an accidental sort of way—taking a class out of curiosity, or buying a video series, or trying it because a friend recommended it. Never lose sight of the first feeling you have during your first class.

Getting Started with Tai Chi

- One of the most common questions that tai chi instructors hear is about where to begin with tai chi. How does one get started? The thing about this question is that most of the time, when you ask how to get started on something, you have a sense of where you might end up and even a little bit about what the journey might be like along the way. But some people in the West who are curious about tai chi don't know what the journey is like—they don't know what they'll end up with.

- In China, people practice tai chi on street corners, in small gardens, and in neighborhood parks, while all around them other people walk by or stand around talking or conducting business as if there were nothing to notice. It is just that much a part of daily life in China.

- The best way to be introduced to tai chi is just to try to start moving in its rhythms. Getting started has never been easier, thanks to simplifications made possible by an approach called tai chi *cao*. *Cao*, in Chinese, means "to exercise" or "to drill"; it's sometimes translated as "calisthenics." tai chi *cao* is tai chi done for exercise or fitness, but you can just think of it as "easy tai chi."

- In classic, traditional tai chi training, there wasn't a lot of feedback from the teacher. In the old-fashioned schools, it also was considered a bit pushy and impatient to ask too many questions. If your teacher wanted you to know something, he or she would tell

People practice tai chi for the physical benefits as well as the mental benefits.

you. And in the meantime, you were expected go home and practice until you got it right.

- Tai chi lessons weren't always fun, either. Old-school Chinese martial arts has a tradition that a good, dedicated student must suffer for his or her art. The actual phrase that is used is "to eat bitterness." It involved hours of drills, standing in one spot until one's legs wobbled, and hundreds of repetitions of the same movement, until the teacher indicated that you were ready to learn another technique. Most people in the West need something a little bit more structured and personable. Hopefully, this is what you experience in the lectures of this series.

- Every beginning is different. And the magic can be different, too. In practicing tai chi, you might be looking for mental benefits and be surprised by physical changes, or you might be looking for physical benefits (such as a new form of exercise) and then be surprised by mental benefits—or both.

• First and foremost, you should be introduced to the enjoyment of tai chi. People who practice tai chi call themselves "players" rather than "students," or "followers," or even "athletes." The term "players" comes from the verb that is commonly used in conjunction with tai chi chuan practice. In Chinese, one says: "Wo war tai chi chuan," with "war" meaning "to play" or "to have fun with." Having fun is one of the fundamental principles of tai chi. For a tai chi player, it is the joy in one's journey that contributes to the joy in arriving at one's destination.

• This lecture series only touches the tip of the iceberg. Living tai chi as a lifestyle is one of the most intriguing aspects of this art, and this lecture has only scratched the surface of the subject. But perhaps, like following clues on a treasure map, you will discover something to enrich your life.

---

10 Tips for Tai Chi Practice

1. Keep things simple.
2. Let yourself be terrible.
3. Knees over toes; elbows over knees.
4. Float the head.
5. Keep moving.
6. Use your imagination.
7. Dance like no one is watching.
8. Square corners should soon become rounded.
9. Check your breathing now and then.
10. Have fun.

Suggested Reading

Kuo, *Tai Chi Chuan in Theory and Practice*.

Ross, *Exercising the Soul*.

Activities

1. Is there a kung fu or traditional tai chi school in your town? Give them a call and ask if you can come for a tour or an introductory lesson.

2. Do you live near a park? Why not drive or walk by early on a Saturday or Sunday morning? You might be surprised to find that there are people doing tai chi. These days, more and more people are learning than ever before. You might be able to find a group of new tai chi or qigong friends to help you get started.

Harmony and Balance
Lecture 3

Imagine what it would be like if you were never bothered by stress again. The stressors of life, including relationship conflict, the pressures of work, and world events, would still there, but these stressors would no longer bother you—no longer trigger fear, anger, or anxiety responses. Worry over them would not linger, keeping you awake at night or making you to mull over them for days. Tradition suggests that this kind of inner peace is what is possible when you learn to apply the principles of tai chi to your daily choices and actions. Tai chi is more than just a martial art; it is also a practical, living philosophy.

Balance and Harmony

- The phrase "tai chi" is like a prefix that can be attached to many things—for example, the open-hand martial art called tai chi chuan. In addition, swordplay is called tai chi *jian*, and the so-called easy tai chi is called tai chi *cao*.

- What unites them all is a core principle and philosophy that says that balance and harmony are the highest good. It's what we call tai chi *zhexue*—tai chi philosophy. The philosophy of tai chi and tai chi chuan is simple: Balance and harmony is the goal, because when one is in balance, everything in life just works better.

- So, how do we learn to make the choices in daily life that lead to balance? Simply put, the dance of tai chi chuan turns the concept of "balance" into a physical experience by taking you through a progression of physical challenges, each one exploring a different aspect of balance. You learn what these different aspects of balance mean on both a literal, physical level and on a metaphorical, mental/ emotional level.

Tai chi practice that involves swordplay is called tai chi *jian*.

- These lessons have a direct application in daily life—for health, fitness, attitude, and peace of mind. Tai chi is a philosophy for the whole person.

- One obvious example of exploring balance in a physical way is the one-legged stances employed in the forms of tai chi—movements like "the golden rooster stands on one leg" and "step up and kick with heel."

- With these movements, you learn a series of physical skills: A neutral spine makes it easier to maintain the one-leg position, and finding and releasing areas of physical tension frees up more energy. Trying to stand too straight with the joints locked out is a common cause of falling over. These are useful skills for aging, if you consider that falling is one of the primary causes of mortality for people over the age of 65.

- But that's only half the lesson. Tai chi philosophy also teaches you that these skills operate exactly the same way to help you keep your balance in times of stress in ways other than physical. For example, being neutral—which is another way of saying "hold off on forming opinions"—helps you think clearly.

- By the same token, a calm and balanced attitude is difficult to maintain when one is holding onto old thoughts or emotions, but is easier if you "let go." Relaxing your mind and heart frees up the energy you might otherwise devote to compassion or affection.

Yin and Yang

- The most essential expression of tai chi philosophy is the concept of yin and yang, most often translated as the pairing of positive and negative or male and female. In truth, yin and yang should be understood as the pairing of any complementary opposites—the ends of any spectrum, one might say.

- The written Chinese characters for yin and yang depict a mountainside. A mountainside in shadow is yin, while a mountainside in sunlight is yang. But it takes *both* sides to make a single mountain. It takes both yin and yang to ensure balance in any situation.

- The following is a list of characteristics typically ascribed to the yin-yang pair: Yang is male; yin is female. Yang is the rising; yin is the descending. Yang is the expanding; yin is the contracting. Yang is the active; yin is the passive (quiet). Yang is hot; yin is cool. Yang is hard; yin is soft. Be careful, however, because all of these states are highly contextual, so what is yang in one circumstance may be yin in another.

- A picture of the yin-yang symbol might help you understand the concept of yin and yang. A diagram called the tai chi *tu*, which translates as "the diagram of the supreme ultimate," is usually depicted as a circle divided by an S-curving line, creating two halves that are often described as fish. In fact, there is a lot of metaphorical art from China that uses two fish to represent yin and yang. Typically, one fish, on half of the diagram, is light in color (meant to represent yang), and the other one is dark (meant to represent yin).

- There are three critical elements to the tai chi *tu* that you must know to understand it. First of all, notice that each fish has a fat end and a skinny end—what we actually call "maximum" and "minimum." This is meant to depict the idea that either side can grow from a minimum, or beginning state, to the maximum. Therefore, the skinny end of the lighter half is minimum yang, which grows progressively fatter to eventually become maximum yang.

- Imagine this as the time span from midnight to midday: 12:01 am would be minimum yang, but the light would grow brighter and brighter until noon, which would be maximum yang. Conversely, 12:01 pm—just after noon—would be minimum yin, and the light would get dimmer and dimmer until midnight, which would be maximum yin.

- The second thing to notice about the tai chi *tu* is that there is a little spot of either light or dark in the center of the maximum ends. This is meant to show that even in the deepest yin, there is the spark of yang, and even in the brightest yang, there is hint of the yin shadow.

- The third thing to understand is that the tai chi *tu* is not a static circle. It is actually a wheel in constant motion. In the real universe, yin and yang are always exchanging places. Yang is always shifting toward yin in the same way that day is always becoming night, and yin is always moving toward Yang, just as the darkest night is progressing toward day. Balance in Chinese philosophy is meant to be understood as dynamic rather than static. Real equilibrium has to be "balance in motion."

The tai chi *tu* is a picture of the yin-yang symbol that represents balance.

- Of course, real life is much more subtle and nuanced than just two states. Traditional tai chi philosophy also recognizes this, so it developed a way of expressing a broader breakdown of balance.

- We start with the notion of the tai chi, the supreme ultimate—expressed as a single, solitary circle. This is complete wholeness, complete harmony. The tai chi can be divided into two parts: the *liang yi*, which pretty much translates as "the two parts," or yin and yang. Then, these two parts further divide into four parts: the *si xiang*. These represent the two pairs of minimum yin and maximum yin, and minimum yang and maximum yang—"the four extremes."

- To make this easier to understand, we can draw these variations of yin and yang as stick figures. Yin is drawn as a broken single line, and yang is drawn as a solid line. Yin and yang plus one more (one more yin or one more yang) create what is known as a trigram, a symbol of the nuances of equilibrium.

- Classically, the eight possible trigrams are arranged in a circle, like the points of a compass—and this is what is known as the *bagua*. Finally, specific energies or images are assigned to each point of the *bagua*, and then specific tai chi chuan techniques and kinetic concepts are linked to those points as well. The eight trigrams are as follows.
    - *Peng*; *Ch'ien* (South; Heaven): that which is expansive, like the heavens.

    - *Lu*; *K'un* (North; Earth): that which is receptive, like the earth.

    - *Ji*; *K'an* (West; Water): that which is dangerous and turbulent, like water in the rapids.

    - *An*; *Li* (East; Fire): that which breaks out suddenly, like the dawning sun rising up.

    - *Ts'ai*; *Sun* (Southwest; Wind): the energy of gentle penetration.

    - *Lieh*; *Chen* (Northeast; Thunder): the energy of division (splitting).

    - *Chou*; *Tui* (Southeast; Lake): the energy of joy.

    - *K'ao*; *Ken* (Northwest; Mountain): the energy of immovability.

- The philosophy of tai chi is a philosophy of understanding the dynamic interplay of yin and yang in any given situation—and, moreover, how to work with it. In our daily lives, are we really paying attention to how much energy we give to yin as well as yang, or vice versa? Even in our thoughts, are we trying to hold on to one state more than another? This creates tension between the natural cycles of nature and our own inner human thoughts and emotions. We have a word for this: stress.

- Life is messy, but it works better when we are in balance. At the end of the day, that is the tai chi philosophy: Everything in life is a step either toward balance or away from balance. When we live in a way that we are more in balance, our health is better, we are more prosperous, our relationships are more meaningful, and our work is more fulfilling. And when we drift away from balance, life becomes more challenging and more difficult to navigate.

Suggested Reading

Read, *The Manual of Bean Curd Boxing.*

Rosenfeld, *Tai Chi—The Perfect Exercise.*

Activities

1. Consider your daily activities. Going to work, meeting with others, running errands—these all might be considered "yang" in nature. Do you give an equal amount of minutes/hours to "yin" activities—for example, sleeping, meditating, or listening to calming music (with no other activities)?

2. Have a chair back or a wall nearby for support for this activity. Stand on one foot, and lift the other knee to waist height. Slowly extend the foot out in a kick, and hold it as high as you comfortably can. It's okay to use the wall or chair back to keep you from falling over. Next, scan your body for any areas of tension—any tightly held muscle. Take a deep breath, and as you exhale, release the tension. Notice how just this simple act improves your sense of stability.

The Ultimate Martial Art
Lecture 4

By now, you've probably discovered that tai chi chuan is a great form of exercise—beautiful, graceful, and energizing as well. But did you know that it is also a deadly form of martial arts, respected throughout China as one of the highest-level fighting disciplines? Every movement in the elaborate dances of the tai chi chuan forms has a deadly self-defense application. In fact, one way to translate the phrase tai chi chuan is "the supreme ultimate martial art."

Tai Chi Chuan as a Martial Art

- The fact that tai chi chuan is a martial art often surprises people in the West. It's partially because Westerners are unaware of the history of tai chi and the culture from which it grew. But it's also because the martial side of tai chi is not typically shown off. People only know about what they've seen, and what they've usually seen is people in the park moving slowly to some kind of dance.

- In addition, there are many tai chi chuan teachers who don't teach tai chi as a fighting art, perhaps even a majority of tai chi teachers. However, the martial arts aspect of tai chi is essential to the philosophy of tai chi—the philosophy of balance and harmony.

- The actual Chinese word for martial arts is "wushu," not "kung fu," as many people think. "Kung fu" means "hard work" (or, perhaps, "high-level work"). It is meant to refer to the attainment of great skill through rigorous training. Kung fu can refer to almost anything—a great poet or painter can also have kung fu, for example. The term is so often applied to martial artists because of their dedication to disciplined training and development. But, technically, the proper term in Chinese is "wushu," which roughly translates to "war arts" or "fighting arts."

Tai chi chuan is an internal martial art, a unique kind of wushu.

- Wushu encompasses all forms and styles of martial arts, including tai chi chuan. Wushu is also the name that has been adopted by the Chinese Sports authority as a competitive event and what has been studied in the athletic departments of Chinese universities alongside gymnastics, wrestling, and ping-pong. There is a professional team of full-time wushu athletes for each province and most of the major cities.

- Some traditional martial artists despise the "sportification" of Chinese martial arts, but this approach has kept the art alive, has brought it to the West, and has produced some world-class athletes and action movie stars, such as international action film star Jet Li.

- Tai chi chuan is a unique kind of wushu. It is known as one of the rare "internal" martial arts. First of all, this style focuses on development of the qi—the internal energy—above the development of strength or speed. Essentially, the theory goes like this: If you hit someone with your fist, it might break a bone, leave a bruise, or hurt a lot. But if you hit someone with your qi, it might cripple or kill that person. Why? Because a person's health—his or her very life—is a function of the internal flow of the life energy known as qi. If that flow is disrupted, or cut off, it can cause serious damage internally.

- Another quite unique characteristic of tai chi chuan as a martial art is the principle that softness can overcome hardness. There is a passage written in the tai chi classics that describes an old man attacked by a gang of young ruffians. Despite the fact that they are younger, faster, stronger, and more numerous, they cannot defeat them. You might wonder how this is possible. It has to do with understanding the flow of energy and using timing and leverage to neutralize an attack. In tai chi, we call it using "four ounces to move a thousand pounds."

- For several generations, tai chi chuan has been included in the Chinese tradition of martial arts competition. In fact, Yang Lu-chan, the man who invented Yang-style tai chi, made his reputation by traveling throughout China and competing in kung fu tournaments. Using only tai chi skills, he defeated all opponents and gained the nickname "Yang the Unbeatable."

- Competition is a facet of tai chi chuan that not everyone experiences—or wants to. Competition doesn't appeal to everyone, and some people question whether it isn't actually counter to the philosophy of tai chi.

- Being a martial arts competitor can teach a person many lessons. One of the most important lessons is to be humble. No matter how good you get, you will always be a student. There is so much to learn, and if you are willing to close you mouth and open your ears, it turns out that even great masters are eager to teach what they know.

- Another lesson is the value of commitment. Never quit, even when the training gets tough. In fact, commitment isn't actually tested until things get tough. Before that, it's not commitment; it's just easy. But easy can also be good.

Internal Martial Arts
- Perhaps the most distinctive aspect of Chinese martial arts is the development of what is known as "internal" martial arts. Most of the vast array of Chinese martial arts fall into the "external" category. There, the goal of the training is to develop greater external properties, including muscular strength, speed, endurance, and powerful kicks and punches. Shaolin martial arts are a famous example.

- In contrast, internal martial artists work to develop inner power—the qi. Their internal work, known as qigong, is believed to increase their ability to harness the inner life force for a variety of purposes, including extending their life span, protecting the body from attack, heightening awareness, and making their kicks and punches more deadly.

- There are a number of internal martial arts, but three are the most notable: *xing-yi chuan*, *bagua zhang*, and tai chi chuan. *Xing-yi*, often translated as "form and will" or "shape and thought"—or perhaps "body and mind"—is powerful, direct, and linear. The physical movements are based on animals like the bear, eagle, snake, and tiger. Many experts believe that the movements were also influenced by the techniques of the staff and spear.

- *Bagua zhang*, which means "eight trigrams palm," is characterized by circling and twisting footwork. The basic step is actually walking a circle, and then bisecting it in a way that actually draws the yin-yang.

- But the most respected form of internal martial arts is tai chi chuan, "the supreme ultimate fist." If internal martial arts are a "higher" form of martial arts, then tai chi chuan is the highest form of Internal arts.

- There are a number of rather unique principles that distinguish tai chi from all other forms of martial arts. One of the most interesting is the principle of softness overcomes hardness. Philosophically, this principle can be traced back to tai chi chuan's Taoist influences, where the superior person is often advised to "be like water." Tai chi chuan practitioners spend years learning to become softer—to release all stiffness and tension. Being "soft" rather than hard allows you to be more flexible, quicker to move, and more sensitive.

- From an energetic point of view, softness has another benefit. According to qigong, wherever there is tension or stiffness, the qi slows down or stops. Because the intent of tai chi chuan is to circulate the qi throughout the body, learning to be softer (to recognize whenever and wherever tension arises—and melt it away) will improve the flow of that inner life force.

- Old-school tai chi chuan training includes learning all the martial applications of every movement. This is known as *yong fa*, or "method of use." We practice every movement to perfect our precision of the movement's application. It lends a certain power to every movement to have it be structurally "correct." For example, deviating too much from the perfect form will mean the difference between it working or not working.

- A person who practices martial arts is called a martial artist, but the term "martial artist" is not necessarily synonymous with being a "fighter." In the culture of Chinese martial arts, the real purpose of being a martial artist (as opposed to just being a fighter) is to refine and develop the self.

- A martial artist applies himself or herself to practicing his or her techniques with a fierce seriousness because an error in the application could mean the difference between life and death. This kind of seriousness is called *chr ku*—"to eat bitterness." It's kind of like the Chinese equivalent of "no pain, no gain."

- But this attention becomes a metaphor for the seriousness with which one pays attention to one's own life. This is how tai chi chuan as a martial art and tai chi as a living philosophy intersect: The philosophy of tai chi doesn't just suggest that we examine our lives; it offers us a way to hone our life skills with the same seriousness we use to perfect our punches and kicks.

Suggested Reading

Crompton, *Tai Chi Combat*.

Yang, *Tai Chi Chuan Martial Applications*.

Activities

1. Do the partner exercise in this lecture—but remember to do it slowly and gently. Move "tai chi–like" into the positions that connect you to your partner.

2. Remember that the philosophy of the tai chi martial artist is that softness overcomes hardness. This can also be applied to noncombat confrontations. Next time you find yourself about to get into a verbal battle, try the "soft" approach. Don't match anger with anger or force with force. Instead, try yielding, listening—nodding your head and smiling. Remember that "the wise person does not contend; therefore, no one can contend them!"

The Five Families of Tai Chi Practice
Lecture 5

I n different regions of China, you will find subtle differences in the way that the movements and techniques of tai chi chuan are interpreted. However, tai chi chuan is not a free-form style of movement, with no standard way of moving or executing techniques. The major differences in flavor and character coalesce into specific styles of tai chi chuan. In fact, around the world, most tai chi chuan players acknowledge that there are five major styles, and these are known as the five families: Chen, Yang, Wu/Hao, Wu, and Sun. In this lecture, you will learn about the origins and features of each style of tai chi chuan.

Styles of Tai Chi Chuan
- One of the reasons that there are so many styles of tai chi chuan is because China is so vast, and for much of its history, regions were isolated from each other. News, communication, and culture traveled slowly—especially because so much of the time, the different regions and principalities were at war. However, inside these regions, there were often individuals and even whole clans who were involved in martial culture and who ended up developing their styles along very similar lines. Some of these styles died out or were assimilated into other forms. Others became prominent and formed the styles of martial arts that are still popular today.

- One particular style of martial arts became the father of what we recognize as tai chi chuan today. This style influenced the development of a series of derivative styles. These derivative styles were developed by later generations of disciples, and they are now collectively known as the "five families."

The Chen Style
- The style that started it all was Chen. According to tradition, the first grandmaster was a man named Chen Bu, who lived in the

1300s. But it was the 9th-generation Chen patriarch, Chen Wan-ting, who gets much of the credit for the preservation and ascendance of Chen-style boxing, because he brought together all the previous Chen training practices into seven distinct routines, which were subsequently condensed into only two routines.

- In the early days of the Ming dynasty, entire villages were uprooted and forced to relocate in remote parts of the Chinese empire. Chen and his family were part of the group of refugees who were sent to areas inside what is now known as Henan province. This particular area was formed by a series of deep ravines cut out by ancient rivers and streams. Some of these ravines had become hideouts for bandit clans, and the new refugees were easy targets for the robbers. Chen Bu, therefore, began training all the members of his village to defend themselves using his martial arts.

- They were evidently successful, because Chen village thrived, and Chen boxing became legendary as a superior fighting method. The Chen village has become a mecca for tai chi enthusiasts all over the world. The village has turned its iconic boxing style into an industry. There are many tai chi schools that play host to a constant stream of tai chi tourists who want to study tai chi chuan at the source.

- The Chen style is characterized by stances that are deeper and wider than most of the other styles of tai chi. In fact, the basic stance is more of a side-to-side lunge compared to the forward lunge of most of the other tai chi chuan families. The tempo of the Chen family routines varies in speed throughout, with soft slow motions punctuated by faster and more powerful punches, slaps, kicks, and grabs.

The Yang Style
- The next family of tai chi chuan is the Yang style. This style is named for Yang Lu-chan, who was the first person outside the Chen clan to be accepted as a disciple and to master the style. Yang Lu-chan was a mighty champion of martial arts, a man who once told a

The Yang style is a style of tai chi chuan that is characterized by a more upright stance and softer, rounder movements than Chen style.

skeptic that there were only three types of men he could not defeat: men made of brass, men made of iron, and men made of gold. He became so famous that the emperor himself finally summoned him to the capital and offered him a job as the martial arts instructor to the royal family.

- You would think that this was a great honor—and you'd be right. But you'd also be wrong. At this time, China was ruled by the Manchu dynasty—Manchurians, not ethnic Han Chinese. Invaders from the north, the Manchu ruled as a separate class and suppressed the native Han Chinese, forbidding them from intermarriage with Manchurians and restricting them to only a certain level of power within society and government.

- So, while on the one hand Yang Lu-Chan couldn't really say no when the emperor offered him the job, on the other hand, he had an oath to his kung fu master not to reveal the secrets of Chen style to outsiders. So, he created his own style that effectively hid many of

29

the techniques of the original Chen form. He made the movements larger, softer, and rounder. The style was still devastatingly effective, but it was also gentler and easier to learn.

- Eventually, Yang style surpassed Chen style in popularity. In fact, today, around the world, Yang style is the most well known and widely practiced. This was due to the teaching of Yang Lu-chan's grandson, Yang Chen-fu, with whom we would probably not know too much about tai chi and qigong in the West. Even in China, it would have remained an esoteric art only appreciated by a select few.

- The Yang style is characterized by a more upright stance than the Chen style. The movements are softer and rounder than Chen style, and the martial applications are a little more difficult to see. The basic stance is the bow-and-arrow step (or bow step), a forward lunge in which the weight is 60 to 70 percent over the front foot and 30 to 40 percent in the back foot.

The Wu Style

- When Yang Lu-chan was invited by the emperor to become a teacher for the Imperial Guard, he ended up training a particular division assigned to protect the emperor's nephew. One of the Manchurian officers in the regiment was named Wu Quanyou and became a dedicated student of Yang. He became so adept that he was invited to become a disciple of Yang Lu-chan's oldest son. It was there that he made some distinctive adaptations to the original Yang style and developed his own family system, which is called Wu style. Wu style is the third of the five families and is a further evolution of internal techniques from the original Chen style.

- One of the distinctive characteristics of Wu style is that it is more upright than Yang style but also adopts an inclined posture— interpreting the principle of a straight spine to mean aligned from back heel, along the leg, to the top of the head. This creates an impression of piercing.

- The moves are smaller and more compact, and overall, the choreography is shorter and less complex than the long forms of either Chen or Yang. Some tai chi chuan historians have suggested that this more compact design was because the armor and official robes of the Manchurian Guard were long and heavy and would not have accommodated the large circle style of the Yang family style.

- Most distinctive of all are the stances. The way you adjust your feet in Wu style is very different. In Chen style, the feet are essentially parallel (perhaps just slightly turned out) in a horse or half-horse stance, and in Yang style, the front foot points forward and the back foot turns in 45 degrees in a basic forward lunge. But in Wu style, both feet are parallel and pointed forward in a relatively narrow forward lunge. It feels very unusual and also provides a really interesting stretch in the calves and feet.

- One of the significant features of Wu-style training is that it often places the body's weight 100 percent on one leg. This is called yin and yang separation. The leg that supports 100 percent of the body weight is actually the yang leg, because this leg is "full." The yin leg, which has no weight on it, is "empty."

The Wu/Hao Style

- The Wu/Hao style is considered by many scholars to be the third oldest style of tai chi—although currently it is the least popular of all five styles. Indeed, no direct descendants of the original Wu family are known to still be teaching this style of tai chi. However, there are still members of the Hao family alive and teaching today.

- Wu/Hao style is considered somewhat rare, and therefore, it is not commonly seen in public. However, the Wu/Hao style has had a profound influence on all the other styles of tai chi chuan and on the culture of tai chi players around the world.

- The original patriarch of the Wu/Hao style was a man named Wu Yu-xiang, a scholar and apparently wealthy merchant who was a student of Yang Lu-chan, the first patriarch of Yang style. His most notable student, in turn, was his nephew Li I-yu.

- This style is distinctive in that the stances are very upright and quite narrow—not much wider than a regular walking or standing position. The self-defense techniques are small and subtle, focusing on grappling and joint control—much like jujitsu.

- The main contribution of the Wu/Hao style is the family writings on theory and philosophy of tai chi chuan. The main reference guide to the theory and practice of tai chi chuan is called the tai chi classics. When you read the modern translations of the classics, three of the five oldest chapters were written by Wu Yu-xiang or Li I-yu, and there is some speculation that one of the two remaining chapters was also written by Wu Yu-xiang and then attributed to the Taoist monk Wang Tsung-yueh.

The Sun Style
- The Sun style is the youngest of the five family styles. Sometimes it is called the "combination style." It truly was a deliberate invention to bring together all the major internal martial arts into a unified system. Tai chi chuan is one of the main three internal martial arts, along with the more linear approach of *xing-yi chuan* (form and willpower boxing) and the circle walking of *bagua zhang* (eight trigrams palm).

- Sun Lu-tang was a serious martial artist who had already studied *xing-yi* and also tai chi chuan under the Wu/Hao lineage. Sun Lu-tang was an extraordinarily influential individual in the history of tai chi chuan and, in fact, in Chinese martial arts in general.

- Although he was born in a peasant family and spent much of his early life struggling to survive conditions in 19th-century China, eventually he was able to achieve a classical Confucian education, learned to read and write, and was successfully upwardly mobile. He survived the Boxer Rebellion of 1900, when hundreds of martial artists were killed by soldiers in foreign armies, and as a result, he rose to some influence as a bridge to the martial arts past.

- Some of his biographers have written that Sun Lu-tang is almost single-handedly responsible for repositioning Chinese martial arts as a pursuit for health and spiritual personal development rather than primarily for fighting.

- One reason he was so influential is because he was a prolific writer, and he published extremely popular books on the three "soft" martial arts—*xing-yi*, *bagua*, and tai chi chuan —in succession. He is also credited with being the first to include lots of detailed photographs to illustrate his books. For the first time, beginners could actually follow and learn the basics of these martial arts from a book written by a teacher they did not personally know.

- But Sun was apparently a philosopher, and increasingly, as he got older—and, paradoxically, as he became more successful as a martial arts master, with schools in several cities across China— he advocated that the real purpose of studying martial arts was to become a better person.

- According to the International Sun Tai Chi Association, this style of tai chi chuan "incorporates the more rapid footwork of *bagua* and the leg and waist characteristics of hsing-i with the soft body stances of Wu/Hao style tai chi … The Form is characterized by quick and deft movements, freely advancing or retreating in agile steps. Stances are high, more upright and natural, with the feet normally never wider than shoulder width. The movements are short and compact with hand movements connected into a corresponding leg movement."

Suggested Reading

Yang, *Tai Chi Secrets of the Wu Style*.

Lu-tang, *A Study of Taijiquan*.

1. YouTube is a great source for watching videos of different styles of tai chi. Do a YouTube search for each of the following styles of tai chi: Chen, Yang, Wu/Hao, Wu, and Sun.

2. As you watch YouTube videos of other styles of tai chi, see if you can recognize movements from your 24-movement Yang form. Try following some of the movements in the videos using your new tai chi skills.

Qigong and the Five Animal Frolics
Lecture 6

Imagine that you had the magical ability to move your life force in any way that you wished, using only the power of your mind. You could restore health, slow down aging, shield yourself against injury, or even launch an explosion of energy against an opponent and knock him or her out with barely a touch. In Chinese culture, this is called qigong. It's not magic, but a discipline that involves developing the ability to sense the presence, absence, movement, and quality of a life energy known as qi—and, furthermore, to condition the mind to be able to seize control of the qi and move it where you want. In this lecture, you will explore this wider discipline of qi—how it is related to tai chi and how you can use it in your daily life.

What Is Qi?
- Tai chi chuan and qigong are closely related. Both are recognized by soft, flowing motions—and to the untrained eye, both look the same. Tai chi is related to qigong in the same way that Kleenex is related to tissue: All Kleenex is tissue, but not all tissue is Kleenex. Similarly, all tai chi chuan is qigong, an energy exercise, although not all qigong is tai chi chuan.

- Tai chi chuan just happens to be the form of qigong that is also a martial art. Many movements may look similar, but unless there is a self-defense application underneath, it's not tai chi chuan. For example, tai chi chuan is (almost) always standing, while qigong can include much more sitting or even lying down. Qigong is not only broader than tai chi chuan; it's also much older.

- What exactly is qi? You can't see it or weigh it. You can't hold it in your hand or in a jar. Western science cannot determine its source or its composition. Yet the entire system of traditional exercise and medicine throughout Southeast Asia is based on its assumed existence.

- What has come to be called "qigong" in Chinese is the craft of "working the qi." The "-gong" in "qigong" is the same as in the word "kung fu"—in fact, in English you'll sometimes see "qigong" written as "chi kung."

- The word "qi" translates as "the life force" or "the spirit breath." In modern Chinese language, "qi" is often simply translated as "air." And in modern Chinese science textbooks, "qi" is the word used for "oxygen."

- Qigong is also central to understanding the tradition of tai chi and tai chi chuan. Some newcomers see tai chi spelled "chi" and mistakenly assume that the word "tai chi" contains the word "qi." That's incorrect for the origin of the word "tai chi."

- But many tai chi chuan aficionados would say that the main benefit of tai chi chuan practice is to develop control over your qi—to refine your inner energy, circulate it, balance its flow throughout your body, develop control over its movement, and develop a keen sensitivity to its presence in yourself and others.

- "Gong" is the Chinese word for "work." Therefore, qigong is "breath work"—although in the field of internal healing and martial arts, we understand qigong to mean "energy exercises." It's a vast field, with hundreds of different kinds of exercises that range from the short and simple to the extended and complex—all for the purpose of developing greater control over your inner life force.

Controlling Your Qi

- So, what's the big deal about controlling your qi? This is your life energy. We use it up and even leak it out. Qi has its limits, and when we have exhausted life energy completely, we simply die. One part of the historical tradition of qigong is its use as a longevity practice, an essential part of the search for a longer life.

- Qigong practice can be broadly divided into three categories: medical qigong, martial qigong, and spiritual qigong. The largest category is medical qigong. In this group, are hundreds of exercises that are done for health purposes—to slow aging, prevent disease, and cure illnesses. Practices we now call qigong were already being recommended in *The Yellow Emperor's Classic of Internal Medicine*, a work that appeared well over 2,000 years ago.

- Traditional Chinese medicine says that all disease and chronic conditions can be understood as a malfunction of good qi flow. The qi is supposed to circulate freely and harmoniously throughout the body along very specific channels known as the *jing luo*, commonly translated as "channels" or "meridians."

- But when for some reason there is a blockage or a leak along the meridians, this energy flow is disrupted. Qi builds up in some parts of the body, like water stuck behind a dam, while in other parts, it is deficient and weak. What is needed is a way to get the qi flowing again, making sure that it returns to an even circulation throughout the whole body.

- The value of these ideas about flow comes in practice. Qigong uses a combination of breath control, body postures, muscle-relaxation techniques, and mental imagery to guide the qi back into proper circulation.

- Beyond medical uses, the "energy work" of qigong and the vast collection of qigong routines and exercises can be broadly separated into spiritual and martial, both of which are directly relevant for tai chi practice.

- The goals of martial qigong are twofold: to strengthen the body to protect it from blows and to build up qi so that it can be used to strike (or push) others. The most important aspect of this is that these skills imply that one develops "control" over the flow of qi.

- To put this in context, imagine that by using your mind you could change your blood flow to move it wherever you wanted it to go. Qi is thought to be flowing through your body just like the blood

© FurmanAnna/iStock/Thinkstock.

Standing qigong meditation involves stationary exercises that help you develop the mental control to move your qi.

does—inside specific channels, just like the blood flows through the veins and arteries. Standing qigong meditation is essentially training in developing the mental control to move your qi.

- Although it may seem to be an unusual—even uncomfortable—position, we traditionally call these standing exercises "meditations." Because they are stationary, they allow us to concentrate on the mental (rather than the physical) aspect of qi movement. But they also challenge us to learn to relax even while standing and holding a certain posture for extended times.

- In fact, mental control of your qi is the central theme of tai chi chuan practice in general and standing meditation in particular. Tai chi and qigong have a lot of sayings—proverbs and quotations. One of the most commonly repeated saying is *I dao, qi dao*: Where the mind goes, the qi follows.

- In other words, all of tai chi chuan and qigong can be looked at as training for the mind and, in particular, training for that part of the mind that controls the flow of the qi. We use both motion *and* stillness to teach ourselves how to sense the qi in our bodies, to improve its circulation, and to refine its quality.

- Again, qi is thought to be flowing throughout our bodies through dozens of distinct channels known as the *jing luo*, or meridians. The value of thinking this way comes during visualization and practice. So, you should try to visualize the flow in your own body.

- Try this when you hear that the meridians—like the veins and arteries—are said to circulate the qi into the arms and legs, around the belt line and chest, and even to the bottoms of the feet. Or take the most important and fundamental path of circulation, which is through the spine. This is technically known as the microcosmic orbit, a loop that connects two meridians: one that travels down the front of the spine and one that travels up the back of the spine and over the skull until it reconnects to the first meridian. Many styles of standing mediations focus the attention on flow around the microcosmic orbit.

- A practitioner focuses on continuous and unobstructed flow. The reason for practicing standing meditation is that our qi flow gets disrupted all the time, and standing can help get it back on track. The meridians may get blocked, or qi may leak out of certain places. If we don't do something about it, the disrupted qi flow is thought to become a cause of chronic illness, pain, injury, and aging. Standing meditation can sometimes correct or reverse these conditions.

- In the context of martial qigong, standing can go beyond just restoring natural and healthy qi flow; it can also increase and intensify its flow. You can learn how to change its direction, gather and store it in a certain part of your body, and also project it as a strike or kick.

Chinese Health Qigong Association, *Wu Qin Xi*.

Frantzis, *Opening the Energy Gates of Your Body*.

Activities

1. Imagine yourself as the physician Hua Tuo. Observe a variety of animals—for example, dogs, cats, birds, horses—and notice how they move. How do they stretch or breathe? Could you mimic the pattern and style of their motions?

2. After practicing all the five animals, think about which animal frolic you enjoy the most. Which one do you enjoy the least? What do you think this means about how your qi is flowing most of the time?

Energy Exercise—A Branch of Chinese Medicine
Lecture 7

In this lecture, you will learn how interwoven the basic theories of traditional Chinese medicine and tai chi are. Chinese Medicine is based on tai chi, the philosophy of balance and harmony. Qigong and tai chi chuan are specific practices that manipulate both the qi energy and the physical body that contains it to regulate that balance in your daily life—and, in particular, your state of health. This lecture will teach you how to keep your body moving and your qi flowing.

Chinese Medicine versus Western Medicine
- The discipline known as qigong involves the exercises of the inner energy. Qigong is a branch of traditional Chinese medicine—one of the main pillars at the heart of Chinese culture. In one sense, traditional Chinese medicine *is* qigong, because traditional Chinese medicine is the science of manipulating the flow of qi—the inner life energy—for medical or therapeutic reasons.

- Its basic purpose is to prevent disease, and its secondary purpose is to restore health. And it's important to understand that these are two very different things. Disease, in Chinese medicine, is defined as an imbalance of qi—either a blockage or an excess. Health, therefore, is the continuous, free, uninterrupted, balanced, and harmonious flow of qi throughout all parts of the body.

- One really interesting contrast between Chinese medicine and Western medicine is how the doctors in each system look at their role and their relationship to their patients. Western doctors tend to look at patients as people presenting symptoms, traumas, and diseases, and their job is to fix them.

- Chinese medicine, on the other hand, looks at people as perfectly operating systems—assuming that they are naturally healthy—and their job is to make sure that nothing happens to disrupt that. In traditional Chinese communities, the local doctors only got paid as long their patients stayed healthy, and they lost money if their patients got sick.

- The Chinese medicine tool kit includes acupuncture, herbs, massage, diet, exercise, and lifestyle, and each one of these is meticulously detailed for every type of individual and living condition. Qigong and tai chi chuan are considered the essential exercise tools in Chinese medicine—often specifically prescribed by a doctor to complement the acupuncture and herbs—because the needles and the tea or pills are only temporary qi readjustment techniques. But it's the daily "working of the qi" that keeps it in balance.

The Fluid Nature of Qi

- Qi is the Chinese word that can be translated as "spirit breath" or "life force." In modern China, qi is frequently translated as "air." In fact, it is the word used for "oxygen" in Chinese Western medical textbooks. But, traditionally, qi refers to something more profound—but also less tangible.

- Like the 19th-century European notion of *elan vital*, qi is an insubstantial energy that permeates and circulates throughout the human body and gives it life and health. Circulation is key to understanding the essentials of Chinese medicine.

- Qi does not just lie inert in your body or ooze about randomly. Healthy qi is always moving and, in fact, is circulating—moving through the head and vital organs of the torso, out into the extremities, and then back again.

- They gather into specific collection points known as the *tan tien*, or single points. There are three tan tien: upper, middle, and lower—corresponding to the head, upper-chest (heart) region, and the lower (belly) area. So, the qi is gathered into these points and then pumped out again.

- Where is the qi pumped into? The answer is that qi is thought to circulate through very specific channels, in much the same way that the blood circulates through the veins and arteries. These channels are known as the *jing luo*, which we typically translate as "the meridians."

- The *jing luo* system runs throughout every part of the human body and supplies it with qi. This implies, therefore, that an efficient and unobstructed delivery system is vital to good health. In fact, the definition of good health—according to Chinese medicine—is the harmonious and unobstructed circulation of qi.

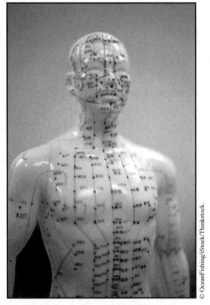

The body's vital energy flows along channels in the body called meridians.

- What constitutes disease and illness in Chinese medicine? Disease and illness arises when the flow of qi is disrupted. Qi imbalances and blockages can result from suppressed emotions, poor diet, inactive lifestyle, stress, injury, and surgery.

- In addition, qi is disrupted by what is known as the "six evils." While early Chinese medicine did not have a Western-style concept of germ theory, early Chinese doctors did observe that different environmental conditions seemed to bring about or foster disease. These six evils are: heat, cold, wind, dampness, dryness, and fire.

- It is these kinds of things that can disrupt the flow of the qi through the meridians and, in particular, can create imbalances in the

43

distribution of energy in different parts of the body. Again, we return to that most fundamental tai chi concept: balance. The reason why qi disruption is so bad is that it creates situations in which qi might be deficient in one part of the body while simultaneously overabundant in another part. The particular combinations, or progressions, of this kind of imbalance is what leads to disease, illness, chronic pain, aging, and eventually death.

Traditional Chinese Medicine: The Mother

- Traditional Chinese medicine is part of the lineage of tai chi chuan and qigong; traditional Chinese medicine is sometimes called the "mother." Like every mother, traditional Chinese medicine gave "life" to tai chi—meaning that it's where we derive the very theory of qi, an intrinsic life force.

- And, like most mothers, Chinese medicine says to us, "Stand up straight!" because qi circulates best when the body (particularly the spine) is in alignment. Finally, mom (that is, Chinese medicine) says to us, "Don't just sit inside all day—get outside and play!" Moving the body is essential to moving the qi, and qi that is circulating is healthy qi.

- An interesting fact about qi is that it is not only a human, or even an animal, characteristic. Everything in the world has energy: plants, animals, and even rocks. Qi is all around us, circulating in the air, vibrating in the colors we see, and raining down on us from above. In fact, the Chinese word for "weather" is *tien qi*, or "heavenly energy."

Suggested Reading

Cohen, *The Way of Qigong*.

Jahnke, *The Healing Promise of Qi*.

1. Have you ever had acupuncture? Imagine the tiniest pinprick—barely detectable—that results in relief from your symptoms of pain or illness.

2. If you want to go a step further, visit a traditional Chinese medical doctor for a checkup. Remember to tell the doctor that you are learning some qigong and tai chi exercises.

The First Pillar of Practice—Forms
Lecture 8

Tai chi chuan rests on what has been called the three pillars: forms, push hands, and standing meditation. These are three different but interconnected types of practice that together bring both mind-body balance and martial skill. Forms are the aspect of tai chi and tai chi chuan that are most well known to the outside world. This lecture will explore forms, the routines (in Japanese, "kata"), or choreographed "dances," that string several techniques together in a flowing series.

Forms Practice

- Many people think of tai chi only as a slow-motion dance that old Chinese men do in the park early in the morning. The exercise that looks to many people like a slow-motion dance are the forms—and are actually a careful rehearsal of a series of deadly martial arts techniques.

- But these forms are also beautiful to watch, mesmerizing and inspiring. In fact, just watching a performance of tai chi chuan can move you to tears or relax you almost into a meditative state. The following are some of the benefits of practicing forms.
  - A stronger body.

  - Better coordination and balance.

  - A deeper understanding of martial application.

  - Grace and beauty.

  - Meditation in motion.

  - Willpower.

  - Kinesthetic sense.

Tai chi forms are strung together into routines, or choreographed dances, to create a captivating performance.

- o   The development of a style consistent with the family.

- o   A deeper understanding of the principles.

- o   Principles in action.

- o   Preparation for playing the push hands game with a partner.

- The English word "forms" can be a bit confusing. It's a translation of a word in Chinese, and it can refer either to a single tai chi technique or to an entire pre-choreographed sequence.

- It's not just tai chi chuan that has forms. Qigong also has dozens of systems and hundreds of forms. But the forms from both tai chi chuan and qigong are guided by a long list of precisely articulated principles, and these are the touchstones that tell you whether you are practicing the forms correctly or not. For this reason, many teachers present the principles like rules.

- The forms of tai chi chuan come in a great variety of pre-choreographed sequences. Essentially, in each different style, there are standard routines that have been developed and established, like a curriculum of study.

- Each style generally involves several "empty-hand" routines, a vigorous "fighting set"—sometimes done with a partner—choreographed two-person practice. Then there are routines for a set of weapons, and these usually include two kinds of swords: a staff and a spear. These were the main weapons of ancient Chinese warfare, and they are represented in the repertoire of tai chi chuan forms.

- According to tai chi chuan tradition, long before there were styles and families, there were the 13 original forms. According to tradition, before there were any of the forms as we now know them, there were the 13 original postures. These are made up of eight energies—what we might call kinetic concepts—and five directions of movement. The five directions are as follows.
  - Advance.

  - Retreat.

  - Look left.

  - Look right.

  - Central equilibrium.

- The eight energies are a little more interesting.
  - The first one is called *peng*, which is an energy of continuous outward expansion. It pushes out in all directions like an ever-growing balloon. It's often described as the fundamental energy of Tàijíquán and applies to all Tàijíquán movement.

- The second energy is called *lu*. Whereas *peng* is expanding, *lu* is yielding and withdrawing. It is the energy of water flowing by.

- The third energy is called *ji*. *Ji* is piercing, as in penetrating or slicing.

- The fourth energy is called *an*. *An* is lifting and pushing—uprooting and letting go.

- The fifth energy is called *cai*. Whereas an is lifting, *cai* is pulling down sharply, like a yank or a chop.

- The sixth energy is called *lieh*. *Lieh* is the splitting energy, in which pulling, or circles or spirals, is applied in opposite directions against the body.

- The seventh energy is called *zhou*. *Zhou* is the elbow strike.

- The eighth energy is called *kao*. *Kao* is the devastating shoulder strike.

- The forms are just one of the three pillars of tai chi, and all three of the pillars—forms, push hands, and standing meditation—are connected and overlapping. For example, practice of the forms is supposed to deepen your understanding of the principles and how to apply them. But to know how well you actually have done, you test yourself in the push hands game. Push hands is supposed to help you discover the weakest links in your understanding of the principles and, therefore, sends you back to your forms again.

- By the same token, push hands prepares you for standing meditation practice. And, finally, standing meditation fuels your forms practice. In fact, part of the tradition of tai chi chuan is to let your qi do all the work for you. It is the mind that moves the qi, and the body just follows the qi naturally.

Focuses of Practice

- One of the wonderful things about forms practice is that your experience of them can be different every time you practice if you change your intention. In other words, what's your focus when you practice? The intention or focus one applies to forms practice may be as diverse as the whole community of players, because tai chi can be a very individual experience.

- However, there are some broad intentions typically applied to the forms, and there are many schools and teachers that emphasize a particular focus.

  o Health and fitness: This is the most common and popular intention for practicing tai chi, qigong, and tai chi chuan. Millions of people around the world use these practices to get their daily exercise, keeping themselves flexible, strong, and able to keep their balance well into old age. The movements of the forms are designed to use every part of your body in complete synergy and harmony in every direction and in every plane of motion. And, while most people have only seen tai chi performed slowly and softly, real tai chi has fast and explosive movements as well.

  o Martial arts: This is the traditional, old-school focus for practicing tai chi chuan and certain kinds of qigong. While tai chi is rarely used for fighting in the modern world, many schools emphasize learning the self-defense application of every movement. Students practice the forms until the placement of the body and the timing of the motions are precise. Push hands is also practiced as a kind of soft sparring, reinforcing the martial focus of the forms practice. Very often, people who play tai chi with a martial focus are also doing their forms with an intention to interpret the moves according to the style of their lineage—the line of teachers going back to the founder of the family they are studying.

  o Stress reduction: As stress becomes more of a health concern in our world today, many people have taken up tai chi chuan and qigong specifically as a way of reducing their stress. Tai chi forms practice is designed to lead you into a relaxed and meditative state. By focusing on relaxation or intending to get into a relaxed state, you'll experience your forms practice in a wonderful, energizing, and calming way. High blood pressure drops, heart rates even out, blood sugar levels normalize—in fact, your entire nervous system calms down.

○ Self-development: This is often a lesser-emphasized aspect of tai chi chuan and qigong practice, but it's important. Every movement of the form is a metaphor for how we move through life. Every slow step and one-legged posture—every complex coordination of body parts and deep squatting stances—ask us a simple question: Am I steady or wobbly? Am I in balance or out of balance? And we can ask the same question about every thought, feeling, and action we have in our lives as well. Practicing the movements of tai chi forms can provide insight into how we lose our balance, no matter what the context. Fear, uncertainty, distraction, and rigidity are things that cause us to lose our balance, whether it's playing tai chi or dealing with life. It is the habit of these reactions that keep us stuck in life. But practicing the tai chi forms can teach you new habits, including courage, groundedness, calm focus, and flexibility.

○ Fun: Finally, at the end of the day, forms practice can just be plain and simple fun. Breathe fresh air, and find a connection with your body and nature—enjoy yourself!

Different Modes of Play

• It is important to note that your forms practice should not always be done in the same way. There are many different modes of play, or different ways you could practice the same routine. For example, with the short form that you are learning in this lecture series, you can employ a different mode depending on what kind of practice you want to get in. The three primary modes are the learning mode, the practice mode, and the performing mode.

- The learning mode is when you are just learning the movement or working out a portion of a movement. It's typically done with less intensity—sometimes it's even just a walk-through. It allows you to improve your timing or memorize a pattern. Sometimes the learning mode can help you discover a missing piece of your form as you walk through it and find a hole.

- The practice mode is when you dig in and do the work of refining your moves and get into your workout. Generally, we can further break down practice mode into three levels: high, middle, and low. These correspond to the depth of your stances, which is one way that we manipulate the intensity of the tai chi workout. High-level stances are easier and, therefore, a more mild intensity. Low-level stances are a challenge; they help you develop your strength and flexibility. The middle-level stances can sometimes be the most challenging, because, for example, holding the half-squat for any length of time is pure qi and willpower. During practice mode, the player works to perfect the form's posture, positions, timing and coordination, energies, focus, and intention.

- The performance mode is when you finally put all the learning and practice aside and just let the movements flow.

- As you work on learning your 24-movement short form, remember to employ every mode and level of practice and not get stuck on any one. This is also a great metaphor for how to live life itself. To everything there is a season—a time for learning and experiencing, a time for practice, and a time for play. And just as you don't want to practice your forms in the same manner every time, tai chi teaches us that life should have variety as well.

Suggested Reading

Huang, *Embrace Tiger, Return to Mountain*.

Ross, *The Tai Chi Companion*.

Activities

1. Now that you have learned several movements of the 24-movement form, try practicing them on a variety of different surfaces. Try practicing outdoors in the park on grass, on the hard surface of a basketball court— even on gravel.

2. If you're not ready to take your tai chi out of the house yet, try practicing with some different background ambience—with music, nature sounds (or silence), or candlelight.

The Second Pillar—Push Hands for Two
Lecture 9

The second pillar of tai chi chuan is known as *tui shou*, or "pushing hands." It is an interactive sensitivity exercise. Some tai chi experts call it tai chi chuan sparring; others claim that it is a necessary precursor to actual sparring. Either way, this game teaches one a great deal about our unconscious responses to confrontation and how to find effective solutions to conflict of all kinds. In this lecture, you will explore *tui shou*, which is very much like a game that helps develop the skills one needs to defeat one's opponent.

Push Hands
- Push hands is a game that uses the hands and arms to push, pull, nudge, edge, and rock your partner opponent off his or her balance—while simultaneously protecting your own balance—because your opponent partner is doing the same to you. In the basic game, there is no grabbing, hitting, attacking the head, or sweeping the legs. Yet this game can knock you on your behind.

- According to tradition, *tui shou* was the invention of the 9th patriarch of Chen-family tai chi: Chen Wan-ting. Chen had been a military man and had noticed that full-contact sparring, which was the primary mode of practice in those days, often resulted in serious injury. Sometimes even the most promising student could have his or her career cut short if there was an accident during practice.

- So, General Chen devised a way to teach the essential principles of tai chi chuan's unique style of fighting without the dangers of full-force punching and kicking. Instead, *tui shou* (push hands) focuses on sensitivity and timing.

- Push hands is probably the aspect of tai chi that makes it most distinctive in any context—whether comparing it to other martial arts systems, health practices, or philosophies. In fact, push hands might be the singular aspect of tai chi that bridges the gap between the martial arts aspect of tai chi chuan and all the other aspects. It extends the martial arts metaphor into the concept of personal growth and self-development. The martial artist takes life seriously, because in a battle, one cannot let up on paying attention and being sensitive to subtle changes. In a battle, if you lose your concentration, you could lose your life.

- If the purpose of practicing tai chi chuan forms is to guide the qi into harmony and flow, then the purpose of *tui shou* is to learn to maintain harmony in the face of relentless attack. In this way, *tui shou* seeks to imitate life, because life and all its stresses never stop.

- The philosophy of tai chi—of yin and yang—says that life is always dynamic. Forces are constantly at work to draw us away from balance, and to flow with those forces in a way that maintains our harmony requires constant awareness.

Push hands, or *tui shou*, teaches the essential principles of tai chi chuan without the dangers of full-force punching and kicking.

- Pushing hands is the second pillar of tai chi chuan training. It's extraordinary in the world of self-development practices because it is one of the few that it helps us get better with a part of life where so much stress actually occurs: in interpersonal relationships.

- Pushing hands shines a spotlight on the fact that almost all of us have ingrained—almost unconscious—patterns of reacting to conflict and confrontation. But finding out that we have a pattern of reacting is only the first step in bringing harmony into our relationships with others.

- The second step is learning that we can choose to respond to conflict in a way that is different than our reactions. In other words, reactions may be natural, involuntary, and nearly instinctual, but as human beings, we have the power to choose our responses.

- In playing the push hands game, we finally discover that there is an opportunity to create a gap between our reactions and our responses—the time you need to choose a better response, one that will lead to harmony. But there is one more step: Once you've figured out how to choose your responses, you have to practice it. It's like a muscle that must be exercised or it will atrophy. And once again, the game of push hands turns out to be the perfect arena for training this skill.

- After the student has begun learning about the basic principles of tai chi chuan—empty and full, the flow of qi, yin and yang, etc.—he or she is put to the test to see how well he or she understands those principles. This is when push hands becomes such a fascinating part of the tai chi experience.

- The student is given a partner, who provides the student with an artificial example of those forces in life that drag us away from balance. The partner pushes on the student, trying to knock him or her off his or her feet. The partner can get quite tricky, looking for all the places that have tensed up or disconnected. The student, therefore, is challenged to use his or her tai chi skills to resist the partner's pushing. It's a game, and part of the rules of the game is to resist using brute force, which just becomes less and less effective the more advanced you get.

- In most tai chi chuan schools, *tui shou* is done in the second half of the class, after both forms and standing meditation practice. Sometimes *tui shou* is reserved for advanced students—although there is no rule about this, and many teachers introduce *tui shou* right away. But there are many tai chi chuan players for whom *tui shou* is the best part of tai chi. All over the world, there are groups that get together—often in the park—for push hands.

- Why is push hands such an important game? What is its use outside of fighting? Perhaps you don't want to be a martial artist. The answer is to go back to the metaphor of the martial artist and apply the martial artists's lesson to all aspects of life.

- The warrior learns that the only way to develop the skills he or she needs in battle, including awareness, sensitivity, courage, and detachment, is to practice—to rehearse his or her responses to conflict and confrontation. The same thing is true in every aspect of life. Mastery of things like better health and fitness, personal development, and fiscal discipline depends on practice.

- Forms practice teaches us about balance and flow, but you might imagine that it's a bit of being in a vacuum. Push hands takes our practice up a notch and gives us the opportunity to practice our balance and flow in the presence of outside, unpredictable stressors.

- Tai chi and qigong forms are guided by certain principles, rules, or observations, depending on how you look at it. *Tui shou* is also guided by specific principles. These principles can be divided into three categories: how you connect to your opponent partner, the techniques you employ to play the game (similar to the moves you make in chess), and the essential energies you put behind those techniques.

Four Essential Skills

- *Ting jing*: The skill of listening.

- *Dong jing*: The skill of understanding.

- *Hua jing*: The skill of neutralizing.

- *Fa jing*: The skill of issuing.

Four of the Eight Basic Moves

- Push hands is a great way to learn to handle conflict resolution in any context—not just in fighting, but in business negotiations, politics, and personal relationships. Let's take the first four of the eight basic moves, or kinetic concepts, and see what they teach us.

- *Peng*, for example, is bouncy energy. Physically, it calls for you to surround yourself with a bubble of qi that expands outward and repels any incoming force. You make your body rounded and your joints springy. Any push against you is rebounded with equal force.

- *Lu*, or "roll back," is the energy of yielding. It's often compared to flowing like water. In the *Tao Te Ching*, it is written that the highest good is like water. "Water is fluid, soft, and yielding. But water will wear away rock, which is rigid and cannot yield." In this case, one resolves conflict by not resisting—by just being agreeable and going with the flow.

- *Ji*, which we translate as "press" or "pierce," is a move that concentrates all the force pushing into a single spot. If yielding doesn't work to resolve conflict, sometimes it's because there is no real conflict—it's simply the projection of someone else's issue.

- The final option is *an*, which we sometimes translate as "push" but is maybe better translated as "to lift and let go." The *an* technique is to really sink down—to get deeply rooted and grounded—and, in doing, so you get underneath your issue, lift it up, and show it the light of day. We might find that what is being argued about is not the real issue.

The Game of *Tui Shou*

- In one sense, *tui shou* is very much like a game, and a lot of tai chi players like to play it that way—they play it to win. After all, that's the point of a game. And if *tui shou* is a part of the curriculum of study for a martial artist—fighters and warriors—then the object is to develop the skills one needs to defeat one's opponents.

- But there is a school of thought among tai chi masters that perhaps winning all the time isn't the best way to play this game. After all, always winning in life isn't balance and harmony. It doesn't honor the cycle of yin and yang. Sometimes it is more important to let others win. For example, it is more important that students work out their techniques than it is to keep track of who is winning.

- And certainly in the realm of personal relationships, winning a fight can be the quickest way to losing a friendship or a love. Besides, what would you learn if you won all the time? The moment of losing is the moment of opportunity to ask, what just happened? And until you have the chance to ask that question, you can't identify the patterns of unconscious reactions that are leading you out of balance all over your life.

Suggested Reading

Olson, *Tai Chi*.

Waitzkin, *The Art of Learning*.

1. The push hands game suggests having a partner, but it doesn't always have to be a person. The first skill of push hands practice is to connect and stay connected, no matter where your partner moves. Try this with a pet, or even a tree branch on a windy day: Gently touch your "partner" with the back of one hand, and then follow their movements wherever they go without losing contact.

2. If you don't have a partner, there are still exercises you can do. For example, here is an exercise that will teach you to coordinate three independent actions all at once: forward and backward in a lunge, rotating your torso side to side, and drawing large circles in the air with your hands. Stand in a comfortable high lunge (right foot forward), and round your arms in front of you as though you are hugging a big tree (fingers intertwining). First, begin shifting your weight forward and back in your lunge while twisting left (as you shift back) and right (as you shift forward). After a few of these, add a large circular motion with your rounded arms to coincide with the body twist. Try this with the left foot forward as well. This kind of coordination of several body parts together is needed to play the push hands game.

The Third Pillar—Standing Meditation
Lecture 10

In this lecture, you are going to examine the third pillar of tai chi chuan, which is known as standing meditation. It is actually a special category of qigong practice and serves the purpose of improving the quality of your qi and your control over its flow. Specifically, you will learn the most fundamental standing posture: standing like a post, or tree. Once you have learned this basic posture, you can practice it on your own, anywhere you happen to be.

Standing Meditation
- Standing meditation is called "standing" because you don't sit down or move around. A central focus of the standing exercises is alignment of the body—along the spine from head to tailbone (and into the earth)—and how the major joints of the extremities line up over each other. Therefore, the standing method is the best way to teach this.

- We also label these exercises as qigong to remind us that this is all about energy. Your tai chi chuan practice circulates the qi in a powerful way, but what are we circulating? How dynamic is your qi—or, more specifically, how refined is it? Standing qigong meditation amplifies and refines your qi, and then your tai chi chuan form circulates it. And then you use that high-vibration qi to engage with another person in the push hands game.

- Finally, we call this a meditation because it is essentially a mental exercise. Although we use physical adjustments to get the best results, standing meditation is really about getting into a meditative state of calm focus so that the part of the mind known as the I— the mind-intent, or willpower—can create a visual picture of the qi circulating in precisely the way you want it to. And you hold this vision for as long as you can, letting your body relax into the pose and tuning out all distractions.

- Typically, standing meditation is done in the beginning of a class. It may last for only a few minutes. In some cases, it can last much longer. But standing is not easy. Your legs and shoulders get tired. Little aches and pains that you never noticed before suddenly become excruciating. Most difficult to deal with is the fact that it is so boring, especially to the Western mind. Everything in your brain is screaming for you to be doing something!

The Main Channels

- In the lecture on Chinese medicine, we learned about the meridians—the channels that carry the qi in its circulation around the body. But although the meridians go everywhere, the main channels go up and down the spine. The spine is the main corridor for the movement of energy in the human body, and in fact, many cultures have a similar theory, including Western medicine, which sees the spinal cord as the main part of the central nervous system.

- There are two channels along the spine, and they are known as the *ren* and *du* channels, which are also translated as "functional" and "governor" channels, respectively. The functional channel starts at the chin and runs down the front of the body to the perineum. The governor channel starts at the perineum and runs up the back of the body and over the top of the head to the upper lip.

- All along both channels are a series of gates that operate like valves to regulate the flow of the qi up and down the spine. But sometimes the valves get stuck, and the qi either backs up or leaks out, and this causes weakness, aging, sickness, and/or pain.

- During standing qigong meditation, one of the most basic visualizations is to imagine the qi flowing through the channels past each gate one by one. This is known as the microcosmic orbit—the "small heavenly circulation" of qi.

Standing Like a Tree

- *Zhang zhuan* is perhaps the most basic of all standing qigong meditations. It basically means "to stand like a tree," and that phrase has a lot of subtle meaning. First of all, it is a motionless posture—you just adopt your position and stay there, as steady as a tree. And you hold this position for several minutes; in fact, some practitioners hold *zhang zhuan* for up to two full hours at a time.

• Start by getting into what Western physical therapists would call neutral anatomical position, with your feet about hip- to shoulder-width apart and your arms relaxed by your sides. All of your joints—ankles, knees, hips, and shoulders—are even and on the same plane. Your toes point forward, you palms are slightly outward, and you head is held upright.

• Once you have gotten into that position—and if this at first feels difficult, unnatural, or uncomfortable, then practice just this for a while before going on to the next step—then proceed to the inner adjustments.

• This alignment is what is known as three-point alignment, and it is a fundamental part of the fabric of tai chi chuan and qigong. First, adjust the tilt of your pelvis so that the tailbone points downward. But keep the buttocks relaxed; don't clench your gluteus muscles. This will have the effect of flattening out the curve of your lower back.

• The second adjustment is to sink into your hip joint. Think of this as sitting down just a little. In fact, in Chinese, the phrase we use is *tzwo kwa*, which means "to sit into the hip." You can always check yourself by poking your fingers lightly against the front of your hip joint to see if it's flat or if you have a fold or crease.

• The final adjustment is called *ding tou*, which means "to float the head." Sometimes we translate this as "suspend from above." It means to imagine that the head is an anchor point, floating upward in space, and the rest of the spine and body dangles below it. The tai chi classics refer to your spine as "a string of pearls" that hangs down from the top pearl, which is your head.

- After you have made these adjustments, check yourself. Are you feeling comfortable? Do you have any pains anywhere? If you do have pains, then you might want to practice just this for a few weeks before you go on to the final adjustment.

Practicing Standing Meditation

- Standing meditation is a little more involved—and a little harder—than it looks. Getting yourself into position is easy enough, including making all the minute corrections to your posture.

- But just try standing motionless in this position for even five minutes, and you will feel the strain in your neck, shoulders, and arms. This happens to almost every beginner. And it's a good lesson, because until you experience this for yourself, you don't fully understand that you are still using your body to make the tree and that you're not using your qi energy.

© XiXinXing/iStock/Thinkstock.

- Some teachers instruct their students to stand for an hour—a full 60 minutes. The body wasn't made to stand like this using only your muscles and bones. But if you don't rely on them, what will hold you in place? The answer is the qi.

Standing meditation involves remaining in an upright, motionless position for an extended period of time.

- Keep practicing, but add only a little bit at a time—maybe only a minute every other week. Remember that a tai chi player seeks joy in the journey, not the destination.

Suggested Reading

Chia, *Healing Light of the Tao*.

Cohen, *Inside Zhang Zhuan*.

Activities

1. Practice the standing meditation posture taught in this lecture. Time yourself by counting breaths. Eight to 10 breaths is a typical minute; see if you can do three minutes before your arms and shoulders fatigue and distract you from your meditation. Every week, you can add another minute to your practice.

2. As you practice your standing meditation, focus on your feet. Imagine that they are roots driving into the ground, going deeper and deeper. How solid do you feel now? This is part of the "tree" metaphor in this traditional exercise.

Benefits to the Heart and Immune System
Lecture 11

For generations, tai chi teachers and enthusiasts have extolled the magnificent health benefits of tai chi. It can seem as if almost every disease and painful condition can be cured just by taking up the practice of tai chi. But how effective is tai chi chuan and qigong practice? Can it really cure disease and rescue people from pain the way enthusiasts claim? In this lecture, you're going to investigate the claims of the health benefits of tai chi practices and find out if there is any truth behind them.

Tai Chi and Health

- Over the past two decades, there has been a lot of serious research done by researchers at such respected institutions as the Mayo Clinic, Johns Hopkins Medical School, and Harvard Medical School (and many more) specifically on what effects tai chi practice may have on a variety of health conditions. The results may astonish you.

- Almost universally, the studies show two things. First, they show that even simple, basic practice of the movements of tai chi and qigong have positive therapeutic or curative effects on most diseases and health conditions. Second, studies show that this practice has no known side effects or contraindications—basically, it is safe for anyone and everyone.

- Interestingly, when we look at specific studies for specific diseases, we see that tai chi consistently emerges as superior to all other forms of non-pharmaceutical treatments. And because tai chi has no side effects, it may be appropriate as an important complement—or, in some cases, a replacement—for drug therapy.

- Of course, anyone who has a serious health condition should consult his or her doctor before beginning or changing a treatment program, especially if he or she is on prescribed medication.

- The three most common causes of early mortality (meaning that you die of something other than old age) in America are heart disease, cancer, and lung disease. Let's take a look at what the research is saying about the health benefits of tai chi with regard to the three most serious diseases.

Heart Disease
- Heart disease is actually kind of a general term that refers to a variety of problems with the heart and circulatory system, including heart attacks, angina pectoris, and atherosclerosis (clogging of the arteries). Currently, heart disease is the number-one overall killer in America today, especially if you are over the age of 65. In fact, Americans overall have a one-in-four, or 25-percent, chance of dying of heart disease.

- The Centers for Disease Control and Prevention lists the following data.
  - About 600,000 people die of heart disease in the United States every year—that's one in every four deaths.

  - Heart disease is the leading cause of death for both men and women. More than half of the deaths due to heart disease in 2009 were in men.

  - Coronary heart disease alone costs the United States $108.9 billion each year. This total includes the cost of health-care services, medications, and lost productivity.

- "A 53-person study at National Taiwan University found that a year of tai chi significantly boosted exercise capacity, lowered blood pressure, and improved levels of cholesterol, triglycerides, insulin, and C-reactive protein in people at high risk for heart disease. The study, which was published in the September 2008 *Journal of Alternative and Complementary Medicine*, found no improvement in a control group that did not practice tai chi."

Research has shown that tai chi practice has many health benefits for such diseases as heart disease, cancer, and chronic lung disease.

- "In a 30-person pilot study at Harvard Medical School, 12 weeks of tai chi improved participants' ability to walk and quality of life. It also reduced blood levels of B-type natriuretic protein, an indicator of heart failure."

- A 2010 study conducted at Springfield College in Massachusetts studied the effects of tai chi on physical function of people who had coronary heart disease. The participants in the study had all been in the hospital for coronary heart disease and had been through a cardiac rehab program. Half of the group was encouraged to continue their rehab regimen and develop a regular exercise routine. The other half was also given 12 weeks of tai chi lessons. At the end of the 12 weeks, both groups were reexamined, and the tai chi group showed significant improvement in physical function. The control group showed no change in physical function.

- "In a review of 26 studies in English or Chinese published in *Preventive Cardiology* (Spring 2008), Dr. Yeh reported that in 85% of trials, tai chi lowered blood pressure—with improvements ranging from 3 to 32 mm Hg in systolic pressure and from 2 to 18 mm Hg in diastolic pressure."

- Dr. Peter Wayne, professor of medicine at Harvard Medical School and author of *The Harvard Medical School Guide to Tai Chi*, said, "What's been interesting to us, however, is how tai chi—this slow-moving meditative exercise—improves aerobic capacity and multiple cardiovascular risk factors. We and others have observed that patients with both heart and lung disease walk faster for longer periods of time after tai chi training."

- "In one small study we compared fast-moving aerobic exercise versus tai chi, which we taught slowly with calming music, and measured the participants' heart rate during the class. What we saw first was not at all surprising: The heart rate increase during exercise was two-fold greater during aerobics than tai chi. But what really surprised us, at the end of the study those in the tai chi group had greater improvements in walking distance compared to those in the aerobics class. So there's something in addition to the increased heart rate in tai chi that is beneficial."

Cancer

- Cancer is the second leading cause of death in America and the number-one cause among people between the ages of 45 and 65. These statistics lump all kinds of cancers together, so it is a pretty broad category. To be clear, there is no research to date that shows that tai chi has any affect on cancer, despite the fact that there are lots of anecdotal stories about tai chi and qigong curing cancer.

- However, tai chi practice might still save your life if you are recovering from cancer treatments like radiation or chemotherapy. While these treatments seem to be highly effective—particularly if administered in the early stages of cancer—they do come with some pretty severe side effects.

- One of the most damaging side effects is the impact that chemotherapy and radiation have on the immune system. They cause loss of bone marrow and slow down the ability of the white blood cells to divide and multiply. This is known as immunosuppression. The national cancer society says that immunosuppression from chemo and radiation is typically temporary, but there is some emerging research that says that it can cause long-term reduction in immune function.

- When your immune system is suppressed, it becomes more difficult to fight off even normally minor germs and diseases. In these cases, patients can end up surviving cancer only to succumb to an opportunistic infectious disease—most notably pneumonia.

- Tai chi practice has benefits for cancer patients. One of the most well-documented effects of tai chi is its positive impact on the immune system. Even just a few minutes of tai chi practice begins to raise both T-cell and B-cell counts.

- In one study, researchers at the University of California, Los Angeles, studied the effects of tai chi on resting and vaccine-stimulated levels of cell-mediated immunity. Basically, two groups—a tai chi group and a control group—were injected with the shingles vaccine.

- "The tai chi group was found to have significantly higher levels of varicella cell-mediated immunity than the health education group. Tai chi alone induced an increase in varicella cell-mediated immunity that was comparable in magnitude with that induced by the varicella vaccine alone. The combination of tai chi and vaccine resulted in a substantially higher cell-mediated immunity than the vaccine alone. The tai chi group also had significant improvements in several secondary measures; physical functioning, bodily pain, vitality and mental health."

- A 2012 study at the UCLA Norman Cousins Center for Psychoneuroimmunology compared the effect of tai chi versus the effect of health education on levels of interleukin-6, a protein associated with a high level of inflammation. Only the tai chi group showed a significant drop in IL-6.

- If we are just looking at how tai chi practices can benefit cancer patients, a stronger immune system can help insure a smoother recovery and mitigate the immune-related side effects of treatments like chemotherapy and radiation.

Chronic Lung Disease
- According to WebMD, COPD—a blanket term for emphysema and chronic bronchitis—is the third leading cause of death in the United States. As many as 90 percent of these cases are caused by smoking. In 2008, more than 13 million American adults had COPD. In 2007, nearly 125,000 U.S. adults died of COPD.

- Researchers from the Ramathibodi Hospital in Thailand conducted a study of asthma sufferers on the possible effects of tai chi practice. After a six-week program, those individuals who did the tai chi training found "significant improvements in peak flow variability, asthma control, and quality-of-life measures." Patients were more comfortable on a six-minute walk and increased their maximum work rate and maximum oxygen consumption after taking part in the exercises. Tai chi can help people control asthma and proves itself to be an effective, non-pharmacologic adjunctive therapy for people with persistent asthma.

- Researchers at the Department of Respiratory Medicine in Xiangya Hospital, Changsha, China, studied the effects of tai chi practice on patients with chronic lung disease, including COPD. Lung function parameters and diaphragm strength parameters were found to be significantly increased in participants who successfully completed the six-month tai chi program compared to their own baseline and to participants in the control group, who only received routine care.

Suggested Reading

U.S. Department of Health and Human Services, et al, *Physical Activity and Health*.

Wayne, *The Harvard Medical School Guide to Tai Chi*.

Activities

1. Pick a condition—any condition, from Alzheimer's to vertigo. Do a Google search on that condition and tai chi, and you will likely find a research report on it. Another good website to check out is www. taichireseach.com.

2. Take the 60-day tai chi challenge (see the Activities for Lecture 12). Can you feel the difference in other areas of your health?

A Healthy Weight and a Healthy Mind
Lecture 12

Tai chi chuan and qigong are two beautiful but somewhat mysterious practices from distant China's ancient past. Over the centuries, adherents have claimed that these arts have benefits that make them akin to nothing less than the fountain of youth. Is this just hype and superstition, or do tai chi practices actually have medically provable benefits that make them a necessary part of a healthy lifestyle? In this lecture, you will continue to explore some of the many health benefits of tai chi practice. In particular, you will examine some of the major public health problems facing North Americans—including obesity and Alzheimer's disease—and the effects that tai chi has on them.

Public Health Problems
- As bad as certain diseases—such as heart disease, cancer, and emphysema—might be, public health problems have the added downside of impacting not only the person with the disease but quite often two to three additional people around them. These other people may be family members or caregivers, but the impact is so deep that it fundamentally alters their lives and life styles. Thus, these conditions become public health issues rather than private health problems because of the cascade of economic, social, and emotional effects they have on the community.

Obesity
- In the United States, the number-one public health issue we face is obesity. According the Centers for Disease Control and Prevention (CDC), more than one-third (35 percent) of the adults in America are clinically obese. In 2008, the cost of the complications from obesity in America exceeded $147 billion.

- The impact of obesity is so dire, and its spread is so rapid, that the CDC has officially declared it an epidemic. And obesity is associated with several other diseases on the list of preventable causes of death—most notably diabetes, which is number seven on the list.

• The National Institutes of Health—along with many other organizations, such as the American College of Sports Medicine—promote a very straightforward approach to treating obesity: Consume fewer calories, exercise daily, and live a healthier lifestyle, choosing different kinds of food, drinking less alcohol, quitting smoking, and being more active generally.

• The problem facing most people with obesity is that they are faced with a catch-22 problem. If the basic solution to obesity (aside from emotional and social issues) is to eat less and exercise more, we have to remember that exercise itself may actually pose a danger to obese individuals. The extra body weight places stress on all the joints, including the knees and ankles.

• Additionally, obese people are systemically deconditioned, meaning that they lack both muscle strength and stamina. This means that they cannot exercise for more than a few minutes at a time and, thus, cannot raise their exercise intensity to a level that actually burns the additional calories they want to burn and then improve their strength and stamina. They are stuck in a vicious cycle.

• Tai chi and qigong may be the perfect answer to the challenges that face obese individuals. These exercises are so easily modified that they can be performed with an intensity that perfectly matches the needs of an obese individual. The intensity and duration of the tai chi workout can be gradually increased to match the development of strength and stamina in the individual.

• A number of studies have been done to see whether tai chi is an appropriate—meaning safe and effective—form of exercise for obese individuals. One study, for example, was conducted at Cheng Ching General Hospital in Taiwan. A group of obese patients who also had type 2 diabetes was randomly divided into two groups, one that learned simple tai chi chuan exercises and another that performed conventional cardiovascular and strength exercises.

- At the end of 12 weeks, no improvements occurred in body mass index, lipids, and oxidative stress profiles in the conventional exercise group. On the other hand, in the tai chi group, body mass index and serum lipids, including triglyceride and high-density lipoprotein cholesterol, had significant improvements. C-reactive protein, an indicator of general levels of inflammation in your body, also decreased.

Tai chi and qigong can be easily modified to match the level of intensity that obese individuals can perform.

Alzheimer's Disease

- Another growing public health problem in the United States—and, indeed, around the world—is dementia among the elderly. Dementia is clinically defined as a loss of brain function as a result of certain neurological disease, chief among them being Alzheimer's and Parkinson's diseases.

- While most people are aware that Alzheimer's disease is fatal—the brain's functions deteriorate until even the involuntary functions like breathing and digestion stop operating—many do not understand how this affects the other people in the lives of an Alzheimer's patient.

- According to the World Health Organization, the number of people living with dementia worldwide is currently estimated at 35 million. This number is projected to almost double by 2030 (to 65 million) and more than triple by 2050. Alzheimer's disease is a disease with compound effects; most of the people with the disease also suffer from depression and anxiety.

- Alzheimer's disease is sometimes called the family disease because approximately 75 percent of all caregivers of Alzheimer's patients were related to them—and everyone with Alzheimer's will eventually need a caregiver. In addition, most caregivers are also trying to maintain a job and a career, sometimes out of necessity to pay for the medical expenses of their family member.

- But the statistics are heartbreaking. Nearly 40 percent of caregivers who are already working 35 or more hours per week are also spending more than 20 hours per week caring for their loved one with dementia. According to the Alzheimer's Association, the cost of caring for those with the disease may be roughly $200 billion per year in the United States alone.

- Common behavioral symptoms of Alzheimer's disease include sleeplessness, agitation, wandering, anxiety, anger, and depression. Officially, there is no cure for Alzheimer's disease. Instead, doctors and caregivers focus on three areas of treatment: maintaining mental function, managing behavioral symptoms, and slowing or delaying the symptoms of the disease.

- While there are a number of drugs and cognitive exercises that are currently approved for use with Alheimer's patients, none of them can compare with the effects that tai chi chuan and qigong have shown.

- In 2012, researchers from the University of South Florida and Fudan University in Shanghai found that healthy, randomly selected Chinese adults in their 60s and 70s who practiced tai chi for 30 minutes three times a week experienced significant increases in brain volume, as well as improved memory and cognitive function, compared to a similar group whose subjects did not practice tai chi.

- The current approved medications for Alzheimer's disease merely slow the progression of the disease or seem to halt the progression in its tracks. None of them have been shown to reverse the shrinkage of the brain or increase cognitive abilities.

Tai Chi for the Future
- While Western medicine has developed some of the most amazing therapies and medical techniques and a pharmacy unmatched in the history of civilization, one has to marvel at a single protocol that really does seem to address every medical condition. That protocol is tai chi— tai chi chuan and qigong.

- What is really fascinating about all of these studies is that they are typically done with novices, often already in compromised health, and for relatively short periods of time. Imagine what could be accomplished if we made tai chi chuan our preventive model and taught it to all of our young, healthy, strong men and women (boys and girls) as part of their basic physical education.

Suggested Reading

Newmark and Geiger, *Chicken Soup for the Soul*.

Wayne, *The Harvard Medical School Guide to Tai Chi*.

Activities

1. Even though you have perhaps only learned a half of a dozen movements, you can always share what you know with others. If you have a loved one or acquaintance in any stage of Alzheimer's (or any other dementia), take one move and just repeat it with them. (By the way, there is no need for them to remember any of the routine; just one or two of any of the movements, repeated several times, is great.)

2. The 60-day tai chi challenge involves doing TaijiFit (easy tai chi) every day for 60 days to lose up to 15 pounds. Do you want to join the challenge? Take free classes at daviddorianross.com.

Tai Chi Legends—Stories of the Masters
Lecture 13

The masters mentioned in the tai chi classics depict great archetypal characters representing the evolution of tai chi chuan through the ages. There are many exciting stories about them. This lecture will tell a few short tales and show the morals each story teaches. These stories—called wuxia stories, which translates roughly to "stories of the warriors"—are meant to connect us to our past and provide us with ideals that we can look up to: the search for truth; the discovery of harmony, perseverance, and commitment; and the careful husbanding of the life force.

Zhang San-feng

- It was a dark and stormy night. The lightning flashed and the thunder rumbled, rain lashing down from the sky. It was the kind of night, the midwives of the village knew, when an extraordinary child might be born—a child with a destiny to teach the world how to find the supreme ultimate—to embrace harmony and connect to its soul.

- The name of the baby was Zhang San-feng. The predictions of the giggling midwives came true, and when he was still very young, Zhang San-feng passed the Imperial examinations with honors and went off to the capitol to become an advisor to the emperor himself.

- After many years of loyal and devoted service, Zhang grew tired of the political intrigue of the court and decided to retire from public life to seek spiritual enlightenment. He gave away all of his possessions, left his family, and set out on foot to wander the countryside. He became a traveler in search of truth and wisdom.

- He wandered the land for many years, having many different adventures. Eventually, he arrived at the famous Buddhist monastery at Shaolin, where the monks were happy to share with Zhang San-feng their version of truth.

- "The wisdom of the Buddha," they said, "is that life is only suffering and illusion, and that in order to free himself from the perpetual wheel of life, death, and rebirth, man must tread a careful path devoid of emotion and attachment."

- To go along with this strict and linear philosophy, the monks practiced a particularly impressive form of martial arts: Shaolin kung fu, which emphasized explosive power; lighting-fast kicks and punches; and deep, rock-solid stances.

- But this was not the wisdom that Zhang San-feng was looking for, so he left Shaolin and traveled on. Finally, he arrived at Wudang mountain, far in the north of China, which was the home of an ancient Taoist monastery. There, amid the mist-enshrouded peaks, the monks taught him a different philosophy of truth. "The wisdom of the Tao," the monks told him, "is that life is pain … suffering, and illusion. But then again … life is also joy, love, children, and all the elements of nature."

- The Taoists believed that all things are governed by that universal force and principle that since before the time of King Wen had been called the Tao—the way of the cosmos. All things in the universe are part of the Tao, including man, and if there is trouble in the world, it is usually because something is out of sync with the rhythm of the Tao. Balance and harmony are the only things that matter, said the Taoists, because in nature, harmony is the ideal state and the highest good.

- "Okay!" said Zhang. "This is more like my kind of wisdom!" Zhang was awed and inspired by the wisdom of the Taoist priests who lived in these high, mysterious peaks. He stayed on Wudang mountain, living in the forest and meditating on the Tao.

- He also began to develop his own martial dance—a new system of kung fu—to express this philosophy of harmony. In contrast to Shaolin kung fu, where the movements emphasized speed and strength, Zhang's new martial art emphasized steady, harmonious movements. He balanced both hard and soft forces and focused on developing the internal strength, the life force known as qi. He called this kind of kung fu "tai chi chuan," "the supreme ultimate martial art." Zhang's dance survives, and today tai chi chuan is the most popular form of martial arts in the world.

- But the story does not end here. Zhang San-feng left a message for future generations. It was a manual to teach the inner secrets of tai chi chuan technique. On the book was written a message that read: "This book was left by Zhang San-feng of Wudang Mountain, who desired that the whole world should achieve health, longevity and enlightenment, and not just learn martial technique."

- Zhang's book is the first chapter in what later became known as the tai chi classics. Zhang's martial art was a powerful and effective one, a dance that is simultaneously a comprehensive fitness regimen, a shield against disease, a way to circulate energy, and a beautiful art form. There is so much to learn about this discipline on the physical and energetic levels that one could spend an entire life studying the dance and its variations.

- But Zhang and the masters that came after him also had a deeper message for those who would search for it. The message is that the dance is only a metaphor for the principles of how to live your life connected to your soul. The philosophy of tai chi actually says that as people lose their connection to their authentic selves, they actually send the entire universe out of balance, which is bad news for the universe. Imagine the effect of hundreds of generations of lives out of balance, pushing the universe inexorably off its center.

Wang Tsung-yueh
- The Chen family was proud of their martial arts; their style was unique, powerful, and—most importantly—secret. The Chen family martial art was a clan heirloom, and although an outsider could perhaps see a demonstration of it, certainly no one outside the family was ever taught this art. The Chen clan had superb fighters

who were seldom defeated in competition, and the fame of the Chen style of boxing spread throughout China.

- Then, one day, a stranger came to town. He was a quiet man who dressed in simple clothing and had the look of a man who had traveled a long road. The stranger happened to walk into Chen village on a day when an exhibition of martial arts was taking place. Standing in the back of the crowd, he watched the young warriors of the Chen clan show off their skills at boxing and weapons play. But after watching them for just a little while, he shook his head to himself as if to say, "not too good," and ambled off.

- But someone had seen him. Before long, the word was all over Chen village that there was a stranger in town bad-mouthing the family martial arts. This could not go unanswered! A kind of posse formed and went looking for the stranger. It didn't take long; they soon found him having a simple lunch at one of the inns. Soon, a group of angry, tough, young men surrounded the stranger.

- The leader of the posse leaned over the table across from the stranger. "I hear you've been bad-mouthing our boxing style," he said.

- "Who, me?" said the stranger. "I didn't say anything. I don't know what you're talking about."

- "Hey, now, don't try to talk your way out of this," the young fighter yelled. "Somebody heard you. Come on, speak up—what do you have to say for yourself?"

- "Hey, really," said the unfortunate man, "I didn't say a word. If you boys want to jump all over the place and waste your energy, it's none of my business."

- The boxer exploded with rage. "That does it! No one insults our family honor this way and gets away with it. Get ready to have your face bashed in."

- The mob attacked … and within minutes, all of them were on the floor, groaning. Some of them had gotten away with only bruises and sprains; some of them were knocked unconscious. The stranger sipped his tea and went back to eating his noodles.

- The young fighter who had been the leader of the posse dragged himself up to his knees. "Master," he said, "please accept my apology. I didn't realize you were a martial artist yourself. You are truly a great master, because no one has ever defeated our style like this before. How did you do that? Will you teach us?"

- The stranger eyed the young man for a long moment. Finally, he said, "Well, I suppose if I don't teach you, then you'll go on doing it all wrong until finally somebody really does get hurt. All right, I'll stay in town for a few days and teach you a few basics steps."

- What the young boxers of the Chen clan didn't realize was that the stranger was Wang Tsung-yueh, a wandering Taoist priest, who had studied martial arts in the mountain temples. Taoist martial arts were based on the development of internal power, the chi—a technique that the fledgling Chen style boxing had only begun to understand.

- When Wang watched the Chen fighters, he observed that they were still using too much physical strength to attack and defend, and not enough mind-intent, followed by qi. Wang taught his students that softness would overcome hardness.

- Wang, who may have been a contemporary of Chen Wan-ting, was probably a member of one of the Taoist sects that practiced martial arts as a path to spiritual purification. The contribution that Wang made to tai chi was a return to the basics: infusing Chen boxing with the fundamentals of Taoist philosophy and the secrets of getting more qi power into their movements.

Yang Lu-chan

- Yang Lu-chan was the youngest son of a peasant family who lived in a rural area in northern China known as Guang Ping village. His family was farmers and servants, but Little Yang (as he was known back then) hated that lifestyle. His passion was martial arts—kung fu! All he wanted to do was practice his fighting day and night. He had found a teacher in the village, and every chance he had, he would slip away from his chores for another lesson.

- One day, his teacher took him aside. "Little Yang," he said. "I've taught you all I know. I know you have a great passion for kung fu, but if you want to go further, you must seek out a great master and study from him. I've heard of such a master, although I'm not sure he will accept you as a student. He lives in place called Chen village. You must go there and see the master. Tell him I sent you."

Yang Lu-chan (1799–1872) modified his martial art style by making his movements larger and rounder to create Yang-style boxing.

- So, Little Yang packed up his bundle, said goodbye to his family, and started out on the long walk to Chen Jia-gou, the village by the stream. When he arrived in Chen village, he found it was not too much different from his home in Guang Ping—a rural, peasant village; people going about their business in the streets and shops; and farmers out in the fields nearby.

- Full of confidence, he marched up to the front door of the main house—the Chen family compound—and knocked. When the butler came to the door, he announced, "Hi! I'm Little Yang, and I'm here for the kung fu lessons. My teacher sent me."

83

- The butler scoffed. "Chen boxing is *never* taught to outsiders," he sneered. "But we are looking for another servant.

- So, Little Yang—hoping to escape the peasant life—ended up as a servant in the Chen family household. He kept hoping to learn some martial arts, but Chen boxing was a closely guarded secret, forbidden to outsiders.

- Then, one night, Little Yang was awakened by the sound of *heng* and *haa*—the explosive breathing done during intensive kung fu training, accompanying every punch and kick. Quietly, he picked his way across the darkened family compound, following the sound. The noise led him to a wall, which enclosed a private courtyard.

- Peeking through a hole in the wall, Yang discovered the master leading a class in the secret Chen family martial arts. Mimicking the movements as best as he could—standing by himself in the moonlight—Yang followed along with the rest of the class.

- Finally, as the sun was just about to come up, he sped back to his room, just in time to be awakened for work along with the rest of the servants. Night after night, he returned to the hole in the wall to watch and learn, and in this way, he began to learn Chen boxing.

- One day, Yang accidentally bumped into one of the Chen cousins, a senior student of martial arts, full of pride and a bit of a snob. He began to push Yang around, bullying the servant. Yang challenged the other man to a fight. While Yang was kicking the tofu out of the other man, the master came out of the house just in time to see one of his senior students being beaten up by a servant—who was using his family's secret fighting style. He was so impressed that he took Little Yang under his wing and made him his disciple.

- Yang studied with the master for 15 years, and at the end of that time, he was such a superb fighter that he became known as Yang the Unbeatable, Yang the Unsurpassable. His fame spread far and wide, and one day, the invitation came to move to the capital, Beijing, and teach his fighting style to the emperor's household guard.

- In those days, China was ruled by a dynasty that was Manchurian, and not Chinese. The Ching dynasty of Manchuria had, in fact, oppressed the Chinese people for nearly 200 years. Yang was faced with a dilemma. He couldn't refuse the invitation to teach the emperor's family, yet he didn't want to give away his great secret martial arts.

- So, he decided to modify his martial art style. He made the movements larger and rounder. He slowed down the motion and hid the application in softer and subtler motion. It was still a powerful martial art, but it wasn't the same martial art he had learned. It was a new style that became known by its inventor's name: Yang-style boxing.

- A funny thing happened when Yang invented his new style, something even he didn't count on. The practice of the slow, large circular movements was an even more effective method of developing qi than his previous style. And this is his legacy to us: a peerless boxing style that trains not only the body, but also the spirit.

Suggested Reading

Buck, *All Men Are Brothers*.

Tsung-hwa, *The Tao of Tai Chi Chuan*.

Activities

1. Stories of kung fu heroes are hugely popular in China. They are part of a literary tradition known as wuxia—equivalent to stories of the knights of the round table. This tradition is why kung fu movies are so popular throughout Asia. When was the last time you saw a Bruce Lee movie?

2. If you like movies, here are two suggestions—both about tai chi masters. The first one is called *The Tai-Chi Master*, starring Jet Li. It is supposedly about Zhang San-feng, the mythical inventor of tai chi. The second is called *Tai Chi Zero* and is about young Yang Lu-chan, the first outsider to learn Chen style. Warning: Both movies are campy and involve lots of unbelievable special effects. But, then again, is that so different than a movie about a king with a magical sword pulled from an anvil?

Reading the Tai Chi Classics
Lecture 14

Since ancient times, the philosophy, principles, and techniques of tai chi chuan have been handed down from teacher to student in an oral tradition. But at one point in the past 200 years, these oral teaching were gathered together in a written work known as the tai chi classics, which are supposed to be the repository of the "true" and fundamental principles of the art and are attributed to the legendary ancient masters. In this lecture, you will be introduced to the writings of the classics, and you will learn how they influence how tai chi chuan is practiced.

The Tai Chi Classics
- The tai chi classics are collected together like a book of essays, or poems. In fact, many of them are titled "The song of" something. Each one reflects the insight or revelation of the author. This is why it's not recommended to read the classics straight through but, rather, a chapter at a time. For generations, tai chi masters have used the classics to evaluate their martial skill or to understand the flow of energy during their practice.

- The Chinese word we translate as "classics" is the word *jing*, and it refers to a collection of texts that is recognized as an authority on important subjects. So, the tai chi classics in Chinese are called the tai chi *jing*. In Confucianism, for example, there are five classics (or *jing*), the most famous of which is the *I Jing*, popularly known as "The Book of Changes" but can also be translated as "The Classic of Changes."

- While you don't need to memorize the classics (although some people do), it adds to the overall experience to know how the traditional principles have been handed down through the ages. In this lecture, we use an English translation of the classics, but originally they were passed down in an oral tradition of poetry and rhythm.

- What's really great about the classics is that they show the wide variety of aspects of tai chi. Each one of the classics focuses on a particular aspect—such as the flow of qi energy and how to attain it in the movements. Others focus on the practical fighting aspects of tai chi chuan and stress the use of softness over hardness.

- Another very important aspect of the tai chi classics is that they track the influences of different aspects of Chinese culture on the development of tai chi chuan. For example, one of the classics, known as "The Salt Shop Classic," is attributed to a man named Wang Tsung-yueh, who was purported to be a Taoist monk. However, this may have been written by one of the founders of the Wu/Hao style of tai chi.

- This classic commences with several lines about the nature of the universe, which is the original context of the phrase "tai chi."
   "T'ai Chi [Supreme Ultimate] comes from Wu Chi [Formless Void] and is the mother of yin and yang.
   In motion T'ai Chi separates;
   in stillness yin and yang fuse and return to Wu Chi."

- It is interesting to note how the language of the classics changes over time. The earlier chapters are very poetic, metaphorical, and even abstract. The more recent chapters are much more literal and direct. In fact, the most recent classic—"The Classic of Yang Chen-fu"—is basically a list of bullet points for correct posture and motion. It took one of Yang's students to add a commentary to explain the bullet points in more detail.

"The Classic of Zhang San-feng"
   In motion the whole body should be light and agile,
   with all parts of the body linked
   as if threaded together.

   The *ch'i* [vital life energy] should be excited,
   The *shen* [spirit of vitality] should be internally gathered.

The postures should be without defect,
without hollows or projections from the proper alignment;
in motion the Form should be continuous, without stops and starts.

The *chin* [intrinsic strength] should be
rooted in the feet,
generated from the legs,
controlled by the waist, and
manifested through the fingers.

The feet, legs, and waist should act together
as an integrated whole,
so that while advancing or withdrawing
one can grasp the opportunity of favorable timing
and advantageous position.

If correct timing and position are not achieved,
the body will become disordered
and will not move as an integrated whole;
the correction for this defect
must be sought in the legs and waist.

The principle of adjusting the legs and waist
applies for moving in all directions;
upward or downward,
advancing or withdrawing,
left or right.

All movements are motivated by *I* [mind-intention],
not external form.

If there is up, there is down;
when advancing, have regard for withdrawing;
when striking left, pay attention to the right.

If the *I* wants to move upward,
it must simultaneously have intent downward.

Alternating the force of pulling and pushing
severs an opponent's root
so that he can be defeated
quickly and certainly.

Insubstantial and substantial
should be clearly differentiated.
At any place where there is insubstantiality,
there must be substantiality;
Every place has both insubstantiality and substantiality.

The whole body should be threaded together
through every joint
without the slightest break.

Chang Ch'uan [Long Boxing] is like a great river
rolling on unceasingly.

(an interpretation, not a translation)
As light and nimble as a monkey,
Set your whole body in motion at once
As though all the parts of your body
Were really one.
Make your tan t'ien a drum, and the gathering of qi a drumskin.
Now tap it with your mind, and feel the vibrations of qi
Coursing through your body,
Like Drumbeats humming in the air.
The Spirit of Vitality is your drummer.
Keep the spirit inside you—don't waste its power.
Carefully pay attention to your every movement,
And your audience will be in awe of your smooth precision.
Confidently extend yourself, but not too much
Carefully withdraw, but not too tightly.
Make your whole body as one.
If you do it right, no one will know
Where one movement ends
And another one begins.

Peng, *Lu*, *Chi*, *An*,
Ts'ai, *Lieh*, *Chou*, and *K'ao*
are equated to the Eight Trigrams.
The first four are the cardinal directions;
Ch'ien [South; Heaven],
K'un [North; Earth],
K'an [West; Water], and
Li [East; Fire].
The second four are the four corners:
Sun [Southwest; Wind],
Chen [Northeast; Thunder],
Tui [Southeast; Lake], and
Ken [Northwest; Mountain].
Advance (*Chin*), Withdraw (*T'ui*),
Look Left (*Tso Ku*), Look Right (*Yu Pan*), and
Central Equilibrium (*Chung Ting*)
are equated to the five elements:
Metal,
Wood,
Water,
Fire, and
Earth
All together these are termed the Thirteen Postures.

- A footnote appended to this classic by Yang Lu-ch'an reads: "This treatise was left by the patriarch Chan San-feng of Wu Tang Mountain, with a desire toward helping able people everywhere achieve longevity, and not merely as a means to martial skill."

"Yang's Ten Important Points"
(by Yang Cheng-fu, as researched by Lee N. Scheele)

1. Head upright to let the *shen* [spirit of vitality] rise to the top of the head. Don't use *li* [external strength], or the neck will be stiff and the *ch'i* [vital life energy] and blood cannot flow through. It is necessary to have a natural and lively feeling. If the spirit cannot reach the headtop, it cannot raise.

2. Sink the chest and pluck up the back.

3. *Sung* [Relax] the waist. The waist is the commander of the whole body.

4. Differentiate between insubstantial and substantial.

5. Sink the shoulders and drop the elbows.

6. Use the mind instead of force.

7. Coordinate the upper and lower parts of the body.

8. Harmonize the internal and external.

9. Move with continuity.

10. Move with tranquility [Seek stillness in movement]. The external schools assume jumping about is good and they use all their energy. That is why after practice everyone pants. T'ai Chi Ch'uan uses stillness to control movement. Although one moves, there is also stillness.

Suggested Reading

Lo and Inn, trans., *The Essence of Tai Chi Chuan*.

Olson and Gross, *Tai Ji Quan Treatise*.

Activities

1. Compare the translations of the classics in the Suggested Readings. Although the differences might be minor, do they alter your understanding of what the ancient masters were thinking?

2. Make a list of any 10 modern-day sports or exercise programs with which you are familiar (such as golf, for example). How many of these have a universally accepted book of organizing principles?

A Superior Workout—Use More of Your Muscles
Lecture 15

Although the health benefits of tai chi practice are extraordinary, they may not be enough to entice people to start learning it. After all, there are plenty of commonsense health practices that the average American still doesn't embrace, such as getting enough sleep and eating a balanced diet. Would it lure more people into trying this esoteric exercise if they knew that practicing tai chi chuan and qigong would give them a flat belly or sexy arms? In this lecture, you will begin exploring the fitness benefits of tai chi practice, beginning with the number-one reason why people typically join a gym or hire a personal trainer: to lose weight. Other benefits include cardiovascular fitness, increased lower-body strength, increased flexibility, and weight loss.

Cardiovascular Benefits
- There is a misconception that tai chi might be really good for flexibility or stress reduction, but it doesn't burn many calories or offer much of a cardiovascular workout. However, in fact, tai chi is one of the most efficient cardiovascular workouts there is, burning as many calories per hour as running or kickboxing. Westerners are not used to sweating and being calm at the same time, but with tai chi, it's completely normal.

- Calories are actually units of heat that we use to measure both energy expenditure and the potential energy value of food. When we work out, we use up stored energy (usually fat). The longer the workout, the more fat we burn.

- In typical Western fashion, we often assume that more is better, so the idea is that if we work out harder (faster, or with more intensity), we will burn even more fat. Unfortunately, that doesn't work; you cross a threshold of intensity, and you actually burn less fat as your body gets its energy elsewhere.

- There is a better way to burn more calories—and it is the secret to the weight loss benefit of tai chi. The secret is to activate as many of your muscles at the same time as possible. Adults typically do not move like this; instead, we isolate targeted muscles in our workouts while much of the body is actually dormant.

- But the tai chi classics have laid this down quite clearly: When one part of your body goes into motion, the *entire* body should go into motion. In other words, even when the movements are slow and relaxed, you are using far more muscles—and demanding far more stored energy for fuel—than most workouts.

Increasing Muscle Strength and Endurance

- The movements of tai chi chuan and qigong are not always slow. But when they are done slowly, one of the great benefits of tai chi chuan is how well it builds muscle size and strength in the lower body. You will discover that slow tai chi can be a really great workout.

© Mike Powell/Digital Vision/Thinkstock.

Both tai chi chuan and qigong help increase your muscle strength and endurance.

- The effect is an increase in both muscle strength and endurance. In fact, keeping lower-body leg strength (and size) as you age is a factor that helps prevent heart disease—a major cause of early mortality in the United States. In addition, having well-conditioned leg muscles help keep us active, allowing us to walk farther, run, and hike—not to mention look good in fashionable clothes.

- But tai chi chuan and qigong do more than just strengthen the leg muscles. In fact, tai chi has its own version of the resistance weight training that is characteristic of Western-style fitness. Instead of just lifting iron weights in relatively rigid patterns, tai chi uses swords, fans, staffs, and spears. Traditionally, real weapons could weigh up to 30 pounds, which is a considerable amount of weight to heft in the body's full range of motion.

- One very interesting version of the many expressions of tai chi is tai chi *cao*. *Cao* is a Chinese word that translates as "calisthenics" or "fitness exercises." Tai chi *cao*, in other words, is tai chi done for health and fitness.

- In fact, this is the origin of a program called TaijiFit. In this program, you use weighted bars and balls held in both hands. It's a great way to experience the beauty, style, and flow of tai chi—and to get a great workout besides.

Burning Calories
- How does tai chi burn calories? Why can it be such an effective workout?
  - First, when you start to embody tai chi, you don't have to worry about getting a fixed number of minutes of exercise, because you are getting more exercise throughout the day.

  - Second, you can repeat the forms you know.

  - Third, and most importantly, when you compare five minutes of tai chi to five minutes of other exercise, you also get more bang for your buck.

- Conventional Western strength training activities are designed to isolate muscle parts: lifting weights. Conventional Western aerobics typically involve spinning (indoor cycling) and treadmills. Tai chi is designed to utilize more of your body. So, the cardiovascular effect is greater because you are adding the sum of the aerobic demands in a much greater percentage of your overall body.

- The exercise benefits of tai chi and qigong are made much more clear when we emphasize total body connection (and total body movement) as a fitness principle. If every workout were designed to maximize mind-body synergy, then even weight training and running would be more like tai chi—greater results, with less wear and tear. They would involve strength gain and weight loss, without losing harmony.

Suggested Reading

Dreyer and Dreyer, *ChiRunning*.

Wollering, *Anatomy of Fitness*.

Activities

1. Take a full class in the "easy tai chi" format that you have done in this course. It's actually called tai chi *tsao*—the American version is translated as TaijiFit. A few minutes can give you a sense of the rhythm and flow of tai chi, but a full hour is one of the best whole-body workouts you will ever experience. Free sample classes are available online at daviddorianross.com.

2. Have you ever gone to the gym to lift weights? Imagine what workouts would be like if you always had to use all of your major muscles at the same time. No more isolated biceps curls; the legs and abs would have to be working at the same time as well.

Eight Pieces of Brocade and a Better Back
Lecture 16

T he fitness benefits of tai chi and tai chi chuan often come as a surprise to people, because most Westerners have the impression that tai chi is always slow, never very strenuous, and only appropriate for old people. How, then, can it be an effective fitness routine? In fact, tai chi chuan is an advanced version of one of the most cutting-edge forms of fitness today, known as "functional fitness" or "corrective exercise." In this lecture, you will learn why tai chi is a superior version of this kind of workout and why almost everyone will love the results they get from it—including better coordination, better posture, therapeutic exercise, and a stronger back.

Corrective Exercise
- Corrective exercise is based on the concept that the human body is supposed to have a muscular and nervous system that supports and is supported by an evenly aligned skeleton. When this happens, your muscles are evenly developed, you have great posture, and you age more slowly. People with well-balanced musculoskeletal development have far fewer chronic injuries and pains.

- However, in fact, most of us do not have this kind of even muscular development and balanced posture, and this is the common cause of many of the chronic conditions that plague people of any age, gender, or work environment. One of the most common—and costly—examples of this is chronic back pain.

Low Back Pain
- Low back pain is the single leading cause of disability worldwide, according to the Global Burden of Diseases, Injuries, and Risk Factors Study 2010.

- One-half of all working Americans admit to having back pain symptoms each year.

- Back pain is one of the most common reasons for missed work. In fact, back pain is the second most common reason for visits to the doctor's office, outnumbered only by upper respiratory infections.

- Most cases of back pain are mechanical or nonorganic—meaning that they are not caused by serious conditions, such as inflammatory arthritis, infection, fracture, or cancer.

- Americans spend at least $50 billion each year on back pain—and that's just for the more easily identified costs.

- Experts estimate that as many as 80 percent of the population will experience a back problem at some time in their lives.

- Chronic back pain remedies are an example of another way that tai chi practice is one of the best fitness alternatives.

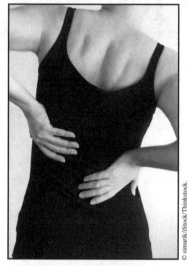

Tai chi practice is a great fitness alternative for people who experience chronic back pain.

Neutral Anatomical Position

- In an ideal world, your skeleton hangs down from the crown of the head, in such a manner that all of the major joints are on the same plane; the toes point forward; and the arms relax right along the side of the body, with the palms slightly out and the spine gently curved in all the right places but with no side-to-side deviations. All of the muscles of the body would be developed evenly to hold the skeleton, without effort, in this position—and this is called neutral anatomical position.

- Neutral anatomical position is the ideal standard of healthy posture and a fit body development. From the neutral alignment, one has the greatest ability to move in any direction or apply force or transfer force to an external object (like hitting a golf ball, for example). As soon as we deviate from neutral, we are already weaker, and we actually make it harder for ourselves to get fit and stay fit.

- Of course, the secret is that no one has perfect neutral posture; everyone has his or her own unique version. Gravity, accumulated injuries, stress, and simply habits of posture—like the way we stand, sit, carry a backpack or purse, etc.—contribute to our own deviations. These deviations become more pronounced over time, until they eventually have a severe impact on our fitness levels and typically cause chronic pain, injury, and decreasing performance. The technical term for these deviations is "compensation patterns."

- For the past few years, one of the most popular trends in the fitness industry has been corrective exercise, also called functional fitness. The main thrust of functional fitness is to balance out muscle development and retrain the nervous system in order to bring the skeleton and its alignment back to neutral—to heal the compensation patterns.

- Of course, tai chi and qigong teachers have already been doing this for hundreds of years. Since the time of Hua Tuo—the inventor of *wu qin xi*, "the five animals dance"—qigong has recognized that poor posture and an unbalanced body leads to health problems and eventually death.

- Corrective exercise has become a huge trend in modern fitness. But tai chi chuan and qigong have been teaching the same principles for hundreds of years. So, you can imagine that it has techniques that have evolved further than other approaches to functional fitness that have been under development for only a short period of time.

- What can we do with this side of tai chi practice? One of the fascinating uses of tai chi is as an adjunct to other sports training. Imagine the benefit to professional athletes if they were able to add a short routine to their workout every day—a routine that would maximize their power and mobility by keeping their body in as close to perfect alignment as possible.

Suggested Reading

Sarno, *Healing Back Pain*.

Yang, *Eight Simple Qigong Exercises for Health*.

Activities

1. One of the eight pieces of brocade is called "bouncing on the toes seven times to drive away all illnesses." Next time you feel a cold, stomach distress, or allergy attack coming on, try this exercise to see if it doesn't speed up your recovery and bring you back to normal.

2. The eight pieces of brocade are a great way to start your day, but they can also be used to get back in alignment (and relieve your back) any time of day. Next time you have a flare-up of pain or discomfort, do just one repetition of each of the eight pieces, and notice how much better you feel.

Lecture 16: Eight Pieces of Brocade and a Better Back

Tai Chi Weapons—When Hands Are Not Empty
Lecture 17

Once a student has reached an intermediate level of proficiency with the "empty-hand" techniques of tai chi chuan, they are traditionally then introduced to world of tai chi weapons. In particular, students learn how to play with swords, fans, and even spears. Of course, there is more than meets the eye in tai chi weapons play. In this lecture, you will learn about each of the basic weapons of tai chi. In addition, you will learn that wielding a tai chi weapon is less about swashbuckling and more about moving the qi.

Martial Arts Weapons
- All Chinese martial arts weapons are generally separated into two categories: long and short. Short weapons may be as small as a dagger, or even a needle. Long weapons may be as large as the 10-foot-long giant tai chi pole.

- Qigong also uses apparatuses, although not necessarily weapons. Instead, qigong routines may include weighted balls and even a thick wooden rod known as a tai chi bang, or tai chi ruler.

- There are two kinds of tai chi swords: the straight sword (which has two edges and a straight blade) and the curved broadsword. Each of the these two types of swords have very different characters, or "personalities." The straight sword is elegant and flowing—often compared to a mythical phoenix, flying aloft. The broadsword, on the other hand, is like a tiger or a whirlwind of motion. In addition, each of the five families of tai chi also teaches a series of routines that incorporate the two tai chi swords.

- What are the benefits of using weapons?
  - They act like weight training: Traditional combat swords may have weighed as much as 35 to 40 pounds.

- They offer specific fencing skills training.

- They improve your sense of timing and coordination by adding objects that extend out into space.

- They help you learn to extend our qi beyond our physical body.

- In the long weapon category, the most common weapons are the staff and the spear. The ancient masters say that the first martial arts weapon was created when man picked up a stick, so the staff is often called "the father of all weapons."

- But the spear is the ultimate expression of weapons; it can do all of the movements of the other weapons—including spiraling like the straight sword, chopping like the broadsword, and smashing like the cudgel. Therefore, it is called "the king of all weapons." An old proverb in Chinese martial arts says, "If I have 100 days, I can take up the cudgel. But to master the spear, I need 1,000 days."

- Easy tai chi can be done with swords or spears. To get a sense of how tai chi swords feel, you can use a few light dumbbells (if you have them) that are each about three pounds. If you don't have any dumbbells, a few cans of soup will work.

- In an interesting way, you might say that tai chi weapons bridge the

Tai chi weapons have many benefits in practice, including adding weight to your training and extending your qi beyond your physical body.

transition between the empty hand forms and push hands play. Suddenly there is something there—something that you have to touch, hold, manipulate, or control.

- Moreover, this is not just a lifeless object, because you are filling it with qi and feeling how that energy moves in your hands. It serves as a reminder that the life force does not end at the surface of your skin or the tips of your fingers. It moves out into space and can be shared.

Suggested Reading

Olson, *Tai Chi Sword, Sabre & Staff.*

Yang, *Taiji Sword, Classical Yang Style.*

Activities

1. Find two short rods between 12 and 24 inches in length (a few rulers or handles from household tools work fine). If you don't have two sticks like this, a pair of three-pound dumbbells will suffice—or even a few cans of soup. Holding these in each hand (but don't grip too tightly), perform the movements of the 24 form that you have learned so far. Notice how it feels to do tai chi while holding a weighted object in your hands.

2. If you are able to find rods or bars for the above activity, try this visualization. Imagine that as you move your bars in the pattern of the form you are sending and withdrawing qi energy into the object. Visualize that each time the energy goes to a different spot on the bar, before withdrawing back to your hand again.

Using the Mind—Inner Organizing Principles
Lecture 18

What makes tai chi—and tai chi chuan—unique in the world of martial arts and fitness? Is it the gentle and circular movement? Is it the slowness of the movements? Actually, more important than all of these are the inner organizing principles that guide how the movements are done and what the player is thinking about. We refer to these as the tai chi principles, and they are an essential part of the world of tai chi. In this lecture, you will learn about five of the most fundamental and traditional principles: yin/yang; empty/full; softness overcomes hardness; alignment; and use mind, not strength.

The Tai Chi Principles
- The tai chi principles are set down officially in the tai chi classics and also in the oral tradition of passing tai chi from teacher to student. These are what we call organizing principles, or core assumptions that explain the mechanism behind a phenomenon or experience.

- To give you some examples from physics and biology, gravity is the primary organizing principle of matter in the universe—from atoms to galaxies (because it moves things toward each other). And natural selection is the basic organizing principle of species diversity, because it's accepted that it explains the mechanism behind species diversity.

- So, these principles are thought to be the foundation of what makes tai chi practices actually work. What's interesting about these principles is that they sometimes seem never-ending; in the same way, the study of tai chi principles is also never-ending, and even if you could capture all the principles in one book, you could still spend a lifetime exploring the depth of their meaning.

- The first and most fundamental organizing principle of tai chi and tai chi chuan is combining yin and yang. These two concepts represent mirror images of each other as aspects of just about anything we can imagine, from people, places, and things to ideas, events, emotions, and energies.

- In the written Chinese characters, yin and yang are drawn as sides of a mountain: yin as the side of the mountain in shadow and yang as the side of the mountain in sunlight. But we understand that it takes both sides to make the whole mountain. Too much of either the yin side or the yang side makes a lopsided mountain. It's out of sync with nature and, therefore, will lead to problems.

- In fact, the philosophy of tai chi looks at all the problems of our lives—every problem—as an imbalance of yin and yang somewhere. Therefore, the practice tai chi, qigong, and tai chi chuan is meant to establish, maintain, or restore the balance of yin and yang.

- This principle is kind of like giving each equal time. When you allow this to happen, you start to experience what harmony feels like. A very important aspect of yin and yang to understand is that yin—the withdrawing—is not meant to be interpreted as going limp or lifeless. In your tai chi chuan and qigong movements, the yin phase is still active and intentional. You are deliberately moving qi in a yin direction.

- The second most unique characteristic—particularly of tai chi chuan, but also of the rest of tai chi and qigong—is the principle of empty and full. This is another pairing like yin and yang, although this case refers to the presence or absence of something.

- The classic example in relation to the body is weight bearing. Take, for example, standing on your right foot. In this case, the right foot—the foot that is bearing weight—would be the "full" foot, while the left foot is "empty." When you shift your weight, your left foot becomes the full foot, and your right foot becomes empty.

Walking meditation can be a great way to incorporate tai chi practice into your daily life.

- Moreover, there are certainly degrees of emptiness and fullness. If you stand mostly on your right foot but have some weight on your left, you could still say that your right foot is your full side. But you could calculate that it is only 75 percent full, while the left foot is only 25 percent full. You could also express that from the other point of view and say that your left foot is 75 percent empty, while the right foot is only 25 percent empty.

- Even a simple movement like walking is actually a process of emptying and filling as you walk and transfer weight. The principle of empty and full is used to become aware of where we are in the process of weight transfer at all times. In the tai chi classic of Yang Chen-fu, one finds that to distinguish empty and full is "the first principle"—the most important skill of the tai chi chuan martial artist.

- The next classical principle is that "softness overcomes hardness." tai chi may have learned this principle from Taoist philosophy, which often uses water as an example of a good way to live. In the *Tao Te Ching*, it says, roughly, "Nothing in the world is as soft as water, yet only water has the power to wear down the mountain."

- Tai chi—both philosophically and practically—asserts that force against force is ultimately a losing strategy. It only perpetuates the cycle of conflict, and even if you are really strong at some point, you'll meet someone who is bigger and stronger. And then what will you do? On the other hand, you could approach conflict with the idea of redirecting energy and force instead of resisting it. The phrase in tai chi chuan is to use "four ounces to move a thousand pounds."

- This is the basic principle that softness overcomes hardness. This really is a unique principle in the world of martial arts. What was the last kung fu move you watched in which the hero claimed that his or her punches and kicks were softer and gentler than his or her enemy's? Yet this principle follows the original principle of balancing yin and yang and makes it consistent as a philosophy.

- Meeting force with force—yang with yang—only throws the system further out of harmony. You may win the battle but lose the war, because you have only created a greater imbalance that at some point must right itself.

- Softness in tai chi chuan should not be equated with weakness or surrender. Tai chi chuan has a full repertoire of devastatingly fast and powerful punches and kicks. They are called cannons and hammers. Before the bang comes the sizzle; the fuse of the cannon is the soft gathering just beforehand. The softer you can get during the windup, the more power you get out of the explosion.

- The next important principle is alignment. In Chinese medicine, qigong practice, and standing meditation, you learn that to get the best qi flow, you need a straight spine. And that qi flow gets kicked up to another level of efficiency when the arms and legs are also in alignment with each other. We call this the three-point alignment and the six-point alignment—technically known as *liu he*, or "six unities."

- To achieve three-point alignment, you can start by flattening out the lower back and tucking or dropping the tailbone. This is known as *lian tun*. Next, you need to deepen the crease of your hip joint, softening the sinews of this joint and opening it up. This is known as *tsuo kwa*, "sitting into the hip joint," or *sung kwa*, "relaxing/sinking into the hip joint." Watch out for losing your *lian tun* when you *tsuo kwa*. Finally, you want to elongate the back of the neck, lift up the crown of the head, and *ding tou*, which means to "float the head."

- The six unities, or *liu he*, alignments are as follows: the shoulder should align with the hip, and the knee should align with the foot. The foot should align with the hand, and the hand should align with the nose, and the elbow should align with the knee.

- Traditional tai chi chuan and qigong are taught movement by movement, and each movement is shaped and corrected based on these principles. The last—and most important—principle is called "use the mind, not force."

- There is a famous saying in the tradition of tai chi: *I dao, qi dao*, which strictly translated means, "The mind arrives, and then the qi arrives." More commonly, it is translated as, "Where the mind goes, the qi will follow." Throughout the classics are references to this principle—that the mind is the commander, and the rest of the body is the soldiers that follow.

- One of the most common traps that tai chi students fall into is focusing too much on what their body is doing. Instead of using strength, the idea is to use the mind. In other words, the higher skill is to master the mind—the *I*, or willpower. The *I* controls the qi; the qi controls the body.

The Five Principles in Everyday Life

- While tai chi chuan and qigong are beautiful to watch and pleasant to perform, they are more than just dancing or exercising—they are deeper, and they are based on some powerful organizing principles. Moreover, these principles connect the physical with the psychological and the spiritual.

- Give equal time to both yin and yang in what you do. Make sure you know where you are before you decide where you think you are going. Remember that water is the softest thing in the world, yet it can wear down the mountain. Make sure that you are in alignment—your actions are aligned with your thoughts, and your thoughts are aligned with your personal values. Finally, don't try to force things to happen: Use your mind, not your strength. When the qi is flowing, the world will open up to you.

Suggested Reading

Chuckrow, *Tai Chi Dynamics*.

Man-ch'ing, Lo, and Inn, *Cheng Tzu's Thirteen Treatises on T'ai Chi Ch'uan*.

Activities

1. Tai chi students are typically presented with the principles as "rules." But at some point in history, they were discoveries. Imagine yourself as one of the founders of tai chi, and just go into your routine of movements that you have learned so far. Play around with your posture, your tempo—even your visual focus. Perhaps you'll discover ways of doing tai chi that enhance your feeling of energy and strength.

2. Make a list of the principles outlined during the lecture. Then try performing the tai chi movements you have learned so far without honoring the principles (for example, rush instead of going slowly, hunch your body instead of standing with a straight spine, etc.).

Mental and Physical Flow
Lecture 19

In the previous lecture, you learned about some of the traditional tai chi principles. In this lecture, you will examine one particular principle from a more contemporary point of view. This is the principle of *lian guan*, which we can roughly translate as "flow." The six principles of synergy and flow are slow down, relax, sink down, be natural/neutral, be continuous, and balance yin and yang. Achieving harmony and balance in your life is a goal of tai chi, and according to tai chi philosophy, *lian guan* is an essential element of balance.

What Is Flow, and Where Does It Come From?

- So, what is flow? Think of water. When water moves, it is healthy and clean, but when it becomes stagnant, it can turn into an incubator for disease and decay. This is precisely how we think of qi in the body. So, flow, in its most basic sense, is movement. And it's not just any kind of movement—not violent, chaotic, or uncontrolled—but, instead, movement that is continuous, harmonious, and synergistic.

- When we think about how we move our bodies, we can apply the flow concept pretty easily. When we learn tai chi chuan, we try to model this principle in our dance. In fact, this is the very thing that is most often said about tai chi chuan players: "Their movements are so flowing." tai chi chuan teachers are always working with their students to help them get better at this, deepening their understanding of the principle of *lian guan*.

- At the same time, this principle applies to more than just your body. *Lian guan* can also guide your thoughts, emotions, and sense of vitality and energy. Mental flow is just as important to balance as physical flow.

Water is a great analogy for qi: Water is healthy when it flows, and you are healthy when your vital energy flows throughout your body.

- So, where does flow come from? How does one develop it? Flow comes from synergy, the principle that says that the whole can be greater than the sum of the parts. It's how all the parts weave and work together that is important, and if we look carefully, the traditional principles of tai chi will tell us how to embrace synergy.

The First Principle of Flow: Slow Down
- The fast pace of modern society causes stress. But beyond, or deeper, than that, the principle of slowing down asks us to pay attention. When we move slowly in tai chi, it gives us time to see everything we're doing. And in seeing ourselves (our actions, choices, and decisions) with clarity, we can see whether our actions really align with our intentions. Often, we discover that we don't even really know what our intentions are.

- This is really the principle of being in the moment. If you think about it, if you're not in the moment, you'd have to be either in the past or the future. Neither of these time frames is reality—the only reality is *now*. Trying to operate in a non-real time frame is one of the major sources of tension, stress, and anxiety.

- In moving slowly through the postures of the solo forms, we open up—and then reinforce—new neuromuscular pathways. These are bridges between the brain and the body, between our minds and our muscles. Thoughts, feelings, and perceptions are also phenomena of neural pathways, and each time we have these unconscious mental experiences, we reinforce those neuromuscular pathways.

- But when we slow down, we get time to see whether our thoughts, feelings, and perceptions are really leading to the results we want in life. Do they lead us to peak performance and peak experience? Do they lead us to flow?

- The principle of slowing down doesn't necessarily mean that you have to live your entire life at a snail's pace. None of the ancient tai chi fighting masters, for example, ever purposely moved so slowly that their opponents could hit them. The principle of slowing down is really a metaphor for being in the moment. In a nutshell, synergy is lost when you are not in the moment, but synergy is gained when you learn how to be in the moment.

- The first key to synergy is to take whatever time is necessary to really see your thoughts, feelings, actions, and perceptions clearly. Practicing the first principle consistently will lead to *ting jing*, the tai chi skill traditionally called "listening power." We can call it awareness.

The Second Principle of Flow: Sink Down
- In Yang-style tai chi chuan, the first movement in every routine is called "Opening the Door." The hands float up and then down as the knees bend to a certain depth—and then stay bent at that level for the rest of the routine, without any rise and fall of the hips.

- This is a metaphor for commitment and consistency. When it's easy—no pain, no fatigue—there is no test of commitment. It's only when things get tough does one really see if there is commitment.

- On the other hand, if you pay attention to the small changes like the subtle rise and fall of the body, you might see an unconscious pattern. If the player rises and falls during the transitions, what is present is an unconscious habit of letting go (even to a small extent) of the commitment to stay down.

- Synergy is lost when you are not consistent in your choices. If your behavior changes whenever a whim strikes you—or every time things get really difficult, you have lost the alignment between your values and your actions. You have cut yourself off from the most fundamental and unique power that human beings possess: the free will. But strengthen the will power by practicing the Sink Down principle, and synergy will be restored.

- The second key to synergy is to be committed to pushing the envelope and to playing full out in life.

The Third Principle of Flow: Relax

- To relax is to let go. In tai chi chuan, there is a certain kind of looseness of the body—a suppleness that somehow never loses the benefit of structure. In Chinese, the word for "relax" is *sung*, which means "to loosen, to relax, relieved, not rigorous."

- A principle called differential relaxation is the principle that every body position, or body movement, requires the activation and contraction of certain key muscles—and the rest of the body should just relax. Knowing the difference between the necessary muscles and the unnecessary ones allows you to let go.

- There is another important aspect to the relaxation principle. One of the unique aspects of tai chi chuan is that it stimulates the harmonious circulation of qi, the internal life force. Qi is said to flow along specific pathways, known as the *jing luo*, or meridians.

These meridians span out over the entire body in the same way that the arteries, capillaries, and veins do. But if the muscles are tight, then it will cut off the circulation, and qi flow stops. But it's not only muscular tension that will stop the qi; mental or emotional tightness is bad as well.

- The third key to synergy is to let go—with structure. The secret to this ability is having distinctions, such as the distinctions of tension and relaxation or even between somewhat relaxed and deeply relaxed. Having distinctions requires developing awareness, the first key. The practice of developing awareness actually applies to all of our principles; you have to be aware of what you're doing in order to master it. Awareness is the foundation of synergy, and the more acute one's awareness is, the greater one's ability to utilize distinctions will be.

The Fourth Principle of Flow: Balance Yin and Yang

- Consider that the whole tai chi form is a dance of body shapes representing yin and yang. Although there are some places where yin moves to greater yin, or yang moves to greater yang, most of the time, the player moves from yin to yang, to yin, and so on. This way, the entire form is a balance of shapes and movements, and in the end, the whole dance has depicted the tai chi—the harmony of the universe.

- Yang is the expanding principle. Yang opens, moves upward, reveals itself, and moves into action. In the solo forms, the final postures represent yang. Yin is the gathering principle. Yin closes in, moves downward, conceals itself, and moves toward stillness. In the solo forms, the transitional midway points between the final postures represent yin.

- How do you get from here to there? The first step is to understand where "here" is. Does this moment in time, space, or thought represent yin or yang? The next step will be to move toward the balance—the opposite or mirror image. Yin moves toward yang; yang moves toward yin.

- The fourth key to synergy is to find the natural ebb and flow that alternates between yin and yang in your life and follow it in every transition in life.

The Fifth Principle of Flow: Be Natural

- This principle refers to the idea that the movements should be "easy" and follow the natural line and flow of the body. If you ever feel like the movements are overly difficult or confusing, then you're probably making too much out of them. We might think of this principle as going with the flow, or not fighting against the current.

- Moving naturally must necessarily assume moving from a position of balance and alignment. The body's ideal alignment starts with a neutral anatomical position, in which we would see the natural landmarks—feet, ankles, knees, hips, waist, shoulders, and head—lining up evenly on both sides. The natural curves of the spine would not be overexaggerated, and the hips (the origin of most postural problems) would be neutral.

- Another meaning of this principle is to start from—and stay as close to—neutral position. The most "natural" position of the body is what we call "anatomical neutral." Every position we create in the body proceeds from anatomical neutral. In tai chi, we're always checking not only the vertical alignment of the spine, head to tailbone, but also the neutral anatomical position—because the movements get so much easier and feel more natural as we approach this position.

- The metaphorical meanings of this principle also have to do with alignment. Neutral life is being in the moment, without judgment or manufactured interpretation. Synergy is lost when we start out with preconceived notions or assumptions. That prejudice prevents us from being in the moment and experiencing what actually is happening. We lose our flow because we are no longer in alignment with what actually is. Synergy and flow are gained when you make it easy.

- The fifth key to synergy is to find your center and mover from your original, natural neutral—physically, intellectually, emotionally, and spiritually. When you start from a good position, you can move into a better position. But when you start from a bad position, it's almost impossible to avoid moving into a worse position.

The Sixth Principle of Flow: Be Continuous

- The obvious metaphor here is not to quit—not to give up, nor to even rest. But here is where we are introduced to the most intriguing aspect of solo forms: that the essence of practice is to perfect our timing.

- Each individual technique in the form is a complex combination of motions of each arm and hand, each leg and foot, the rotation of the torso, and even the turning of the head and eyes. All the pieces ideally must commence motion at the same time and arrive at their final positions and stop motion at the same time. However, each body part is a different length and a different weight and must travel a different distance—often in opposite directions.

- This is perhaps the most powerful metaphor of the six basic principles. In our culture, we are taught to think linearly about our lives. We're encouraged to set priorities and to decide what is most important, and then next most important, and so on.

- But the sixth basic principle offers an alternative point of view: Everything is an equal priority. After all, life really does come at us all at once, so setting linear priorities is a defiance of the fifth principle, "be natural."

- Instead of setting priorities, then, the tai chi key to synergy is to master the timing of everything. Flow is lost when you try to prioritize; flow is also lost when you are overwhelmed. Flow is gained when you learn how to coordinate your movements so that everything begins and ends at the same time. As we learn in perfecting the solo forms, it is possible to set all things in motion at the same time and coordinate their completion at the same precise moment. It just takes practice.

- The sixth key to synergy is to practice timing and coordination—whether it's the timing of the movements of your body or the coordination of the relationships and events of your life.

Suggested Reading

Ross, *Power, Freedom and Flow.*

Slingerland, *Trying Not to Try.*

Activities

1. Most of us have heard the advice to "be in the moment." But not all of us have ever learned *how* to be in the moment, which is also the first rule of the principle of flow. Next time you experience a situation that doesn't go as smoothly and effortlessly as you want it to, notice where your thoughts went. Did you start anticipating that this would affect something else down the road (thinking about the future)? Or did you flash back to a memory of a similar situation in which not all went as smooth as silk (thinking about the past)?

2. For this exercise, you will need a pair of small dumbbells, between two and five pounds. If you don't have any of these on hand, a few cans of soup will do. Holding one of the dumbbells in each hand, go through all of the movements you've learned so far of the 24-movement form. As soon as you are done, put the weights down and perform the movements again. Notice how light your hands feel now—almost like they were weightless and could float away by themselves. This is what "effortless" feels like.

Creating Space for Choices
Lecture 20

A t this point in the course, you should be familiar with the many benefits of tai chi and tai chi chuan. But tai chi is more than an exercise to be practiced a few times a week. The great masters of tai chi chuan teach that it can be a lifestyle that infuses our every action and influences our every choice. What would that kind of a life look like? In this lecture, you will find out how to live tai chi as a lifestyle, and you will learn a tai chi exercise that illustrates how the movements you are learning lead to the ability to overcome stress and anxiety.

A Living Philosophy

• Tai chi chuan has often been called a "living philosophy." In other words, it is a philosophy that can be applied to practical matters—an approach that really works on a daily basis, not just one that is written in a dusty book. What differentiates this from other philosophical systems is that tai chi will back up every philosophical point with both an organizing principle and a physical rehearsal method.

• The practice of tai chi chuan on a daily basis teaches you all you need to know about living your life according to this philosophy—and getting the results that this philosophy promises. The philosophy is simple: Embrace balance in all things. And the promise is that your life will work better; your health, prosperity, and relationships will be better. It is a simple concept: When you are in balance, everything works better. And when you are out of balance, everything begins to fall apart.

• But what is it that throws us out of balance? In a word, stress. Stress comes in a million different forms, shapes, and sizes. Stress is big and in our face, and it's small and nibbles at the corners of our lives in a way we don't notice, yet it takes its toll.

- Think of stress like the force of gravity: unseen and unfelt, yet ubiquitous and unresting. Gravity is working on you 24 hours a day, 7 days a week, 365 days a year. Gravity makes you older, pulling down on your organs, muscles, and skin. Gravity makes you slower: It's a force you are always moving against as you walk, run, or leap. The force of gravity keeps us from flying. Gravity, in fact, can be described as the primary physical stressor to life on earth as a human being.

- Embracing the practical, living philosophy of tai chi depends on our ability to make instantaneous choices. Every moment of life is like a crossroad, at which we have the power to make choices that lead us either toward balance and harmony or away from them.

- There are no meaningless or irrelevant choice points, so we must be ever vigilant. Here is where the tradition of the martial artist comes in. In a fight or a battle, the warrior must pay attention to everything. To let his or her attention falter may be the difference between life and death. When we approach life with the attention and dedication of the samurai, we make better choices a habit—a lifestyle.

- These "better choices" we make must be made on the basis of some specific assessment. The tai chi artist is always sensitive to the flow of qi and balance of the surroundings. He or she is (in effect) always aware of the qi of every situation. If the flow is not right, or doesn't support one's personal balance, then one must make an adjustment to change the balance.

Making Better Choices in Life

- In order to make a habit of making better choices, we have to learn to create a space between our reactions and our responses. It's in that space—that gap—that the tai chi artist is able to choose an action that promotes or maintains harmony.

- Here we use our physical movements to practice the principle of sinking and rooting. In Chinese, there is the phrase *Chen dao di*:

"When you sink, sink to the earth." At the end of every movement, exhale, and in that slight pause, feel yourself getting really heavy and sinking down into the earth. From there, the transition into the next movement is calmer, more mindful—make it a choice, not a reaction.

- An example in real life is arguing with a spouse. Often disagreements escalate into fights that go on for years. Little annoyances that would never have been noticed in the honeymoon phase now trigger an explosion of rage. But why? The answer is tension—stress.

- Very often the cause of an argument gets conflated with the person you are arguing with. The stress and anxiety that might appropriately be associated with one now gets triggered by the mere presence of the other. There is actually a neurological basis for this, known as Hebb's law, named for Canadian neuroscientist Donald Hebb. Hebb's law states that neurons that fire together at one time will

Stress can lead to arguments between couples, and tai chi practice can help eliminate stress.

tend to fire together in the future. This idea was later paraphrased by Carla Shatz as "Neurons that fire together, wire together."

- So, if stress over finances—one of the most commonly cited causes of marital strife—causes you to snap at your spouse, and that snap turns into an angry argument, then over time, just the fact that your spouse walks into the room begins to stimulate the same nervous system reactions that were originally caused by anxiety over money, and you snap for no reason, without even being aware of it.

- But to live the tai chi lifestyle means that you *are* aware of your triggers, reactions, and responses all the time. Tai chi "life artists"— like tai chi martial artists—train themselves to be sensitive to subtle changes in energy within themselves, in the interactions between themselves and others, and in the interactions between themselves and the environment around them.

- Tai chi chuan masters are unique in that they recognize that they have a choice in how they respond to an attack. Rather than trying to match strength with an opponent or use force against force, tai chi masters choose to use "four ounces to move a thousand pounds." Softness overcomes hardness, not more hardness. The end goal is to restore harmony. And the basic tai chi chuan organizing principles are the key to making choices that lead to balance and harmony.

- Give equal time to both yin and yang in what you do. Make sure you know where you are before you decide where you think you are going. Remember that water is the softest thing in the world, yet it can wear down the mountain. Make sure that you are in alignment—your actions are aligned with your thoughts, and your thoughts are aligned with your personal values. Finally, don't try to force things to happen: Use your mind, not your strength.

- Heaven, human, and home (earth) are the three treasures. What's going on with spirit, with mind, and with the body? These are the questions that the living philosophy of tai chi teaches you to ask and answer, in that gap between reaction and response. But it takes practice—rehearsal.

- That's why we make our forms practice, our push hands, and our standing meditation a part of our day as much as having lunch or brushing our teeth. Our daily practice doesn't have to be long, and it doesn't have to be grueling. In fact, tai chi was meant to be played, not worked.

Suggested Reading

Leonard, *Mastery*.

———, *The Way of Aikido*.

Activities

1. One of the strongest themes that runs through the principles of tai chi and qigong is "alignment." Most fundamentally, this principle refers to the (relaxed) straightness of your posture, so that your qi can flow smoothly up and down the spine. But we can also see alignment as a metaphor—most fundamentally referring to whether our actions match our thoughts and words. During the coming week, make note of how many times you do things that you have said or thought that you would not—or fail to do things you said or thought that you would. In these cases, you could say that you are "out of alignment."

2. It is typically American to "work hard." But consider that maybe you could actually accomplish more—and enjoy your work more—if you worked "softer." Next time you have a physical task to do (such as folding laundry or washing dishes, for example), try exerting a little less and flow through it "softly." Tip: Take many deep breaths throughout to release tension.

Flow at Work—When Business Is in Balance
Lecture 21

W hen we talk about tai chi and qigong, we are not limiting our conversations to physical or therapeutic exercises—activities that are only done in a class or training environment—but, rather, a way of living that guides all the aspects of your life into greater balance. One of the places where we spend so much of our time and energy is at work—our daily jobs and careers. This is a perfect example of how tai chi can guide and benefit real life. In this lecture, you will explore the possibilities behind tai chi practices on the job.

Workplace Wellness
- We spend most of our waking hours at work. All of the things that take a toll on the body—inactivity, sitting for long periods of time in a chair, hours of stress, typically terrible food—all happen at work. All that wear and tear diminishes productivity, job satisfaction, and happiness.

- In fact, absenteeism—work days lost because of workplace illness, stress, burnout, injury, and depression—amounts to about $84 billion per year, according to the Gallup-Healthways Well-Being Index poll. Logically, it would be nice to include something in the workplace to offset all that stress.

- Indeed, there is a rising trend of businesses investing in workplace wellness. But workplace wellness programs can be difficult to implement and maintain. Where will you hold your workouts? How much time away from your desks will you require? Does the program really help with stress? What about helping with burnout and depression?

- At this point in the course, you have learned a lot about the health and fitness benefits of tai chi. Obviously, tai chi chuan and qigong are proven to have all the health and fitness benefits that a workplace wellness program needs: They reduce stress and anxiety, elevate mood, and seem to even increase happiness.

- Tai chi chuan and qigong are the perfect heart-healthy cardiovascular workouts for the workplace—lowering blood pressure and improving the immune system to ward off those unwanted sick days. They even improve memory, attention, and creativity.

- But perhaps even more importantly, tai chi practices just fit into the workplace. Tai chi chuan and qigong don't require any special equipment or dedicated workout space. They can even be done in a cubicle or behind a desk. In fact, you can do this with others, each in your own cubicle.

- In the workplace, hundreds of decisions need to be made every day to plan, execute, and evaluate business practices. And it's obvious that the desired outcome of these decisions is greater success for both the business itself and the individuals who work there. But how often do business people consider that business success follows the same basic rule as individual health and happiness?

- Balance is the key. When a business is in balance, then everything works better. When a business is out of balance, then things begin to break down or become more of a struggle. Inexplicably, certain areas of work take more time or effort than they used to—or seem that they ought to. The solution, therefore, is to bring the principles of tai chi to bear on the business. The basic principles of balance can be expressed and understood in contemporary terms.

- Harmony is a condition that is created by the even and equal interweaving of three things: power (or vitality), freedom (or absence of constraint), and flow (or complete connectedness). And each one of these has a source: Power is what you get when you plug all the leaks, and we call that "integrity." Freedom is what you get when you stop being judgmental, and we call that "compassion." And flow is what you get when you not only connect all the parts, but you also allow them to work together harmoniously, and we call that "synergy."

Incorporating Tai Chi into the Work Culture

- How can we make these principles a part of work culture?
  - What gets rewarded is alignment, with the actual mission statement of the organization.

  - Let go—to have corporate relaxation. Let go of what didn't work last quarter, or let go of a bad meeting. Experience it, but let go.

  - Be in the moment. Focus on the here and now. Get motivated by the opportunities in the present moment.

  - Visualize. Get really good at making the picture of what you want.

Tai chi chuan and qigong can create balance and harmony in the workplace.

- Innovation is the business equivalent of freedom. Because judgment is what kills innovation, members of the company can allow each other to express their vision, at least initially, without judgment. In tai chi terms, you have to first connect and follow the other in order to understand him or her.

- Finally, teamwork is analogous to flow—where the whole is greater than the sum of the parts. Combine chi with another person. Great teams provide creative results far beyond what each individual could accomplish, but this only happens when there is synergy.

- And what might help a company adopt or implement these principles into their corporate structure? A company-wide opportunity to practice the movements of tai chi chuan. Tai chi practices, once thought of as only an esoteric form of Chinese martial arts and meditation, can actually contribute solutions to a multibillion-dollar problem in our economy.

Suggested Reading

Huang and Lynch, *Thinking Body, Dancing Mind.*

Kaye, *Zen at Work.*

Activity

1. Organize a simple push hands meeting at your office. Get the executives to pair up with the rest of the staff. Ask them to start with the most basic exercise—to connect and just follow. Assign one person as the "leader" and one as the "follower." But monitor the exercise closely; you'll probably catch the executive "follower" trying to take over and lead.

Energy Flow in Your Surroundings
Lecture 22

The principles of feng shui and the theory of five elements are key to understanding how tai chi practices work both on the level of physical health and well-being *and* on the level of living the tai chi lifestyle, in a wider environment. A smooth and healthy flow of qi is a primary requirement for balance and harmony. Feng shui is a qi-balancing technique for the environment in which you live, and qigong and tai chi chuan are qi-balancing techniques for your inner landscape.

The Flow of Qi

- Wind and water are substances that flow. They are the softest elements in the world—barely tangible in some cases—yet they have the power to wear away mountains and carve deep canyons. They nurture us; fresh air and clean water are essential for life. Yet we require them in somewhat of a delicate balance, because in either their absence or overabundance, we might find disaster. In this way, they are companions to the substance known as qi, the life energy of qigong and tai chi chuan, which also flows.

- "Wind and water," in the Chinese language, is feng shui—the ancient Taoist science of manipulating or designing our environment so that wind, water, and qi energy can flow in just the right amounts and in the most beneficial way in our lives.

- From the beginning of this course, you have been practicing and learning about qigong—the ancient Chinese craft of manipulating the inner life force, the qi—for health, self-defense, and spiritual development. By learning certain breathing and visualization techniques, you learn how to improve the circulation of qi throughout all parts of your body, slowing the process of aging and improving your health and fitness.

- But what would it be like to be able to change the flow of qi in your house, yard, and place of business? Is it possible to use qigong to improve the "health" of your marriage, career, and finances? In this lecture, you learn about the art of feng shui, an ancient Chinese method of harmonizing the flow of qi in our surrounding environment. You also get an introduction to something called the five elements theory, an integral part of traditional Chinese medicine, qigong, tai chi chuan—and feng shui.

Feng Shui

- Feng shui is the science of determining how qi is flowing through your environment and whether that qi flow can be improved. Feng shui translates as "wind and water"—two natural elements that are able to flow—so we think of the metaphors as whether qi is moving well or not.

- Feng shui has been used in Asia for thousands of years to orient the construction of the emperors' palaces and tombs, canals and dock

© Pavel Timofeyev/iStock/Thinkstock.

Feng shui is the science of analyzing qi flow in your environment.

works, and temples. Today, it is still very popular all over the world and is often used in planning the construction, or interior design, of homes and businesses.

- Feng shui is based on an extension of the qi theory you've been learning about in the context of Chinese medicine: that there is an energy that flows throughout the human body and keeps us vital and alive.

- But in Chinese culture, qi is not confined to the body. Qi actually flows everywhere. Qi is all around us, especially in green and living things like plants and animals. It interacts with us constantly in our outer environment. The Chinese word for "weather" is *tien qi*—"life force of heaven," or "qi of the sky."

- Feng shui works because of the theory that in just the same way that qi can get stuck (blocked) in the body, or leak out somewhere, the qi in the environment can be blocked, stuck, or blown off course. And in the same way that a qi doctor will use needles, herbs, or qigong to move your body's qi, a feng shui master will use objects, plants, animals, color, etc., to move your environmental qi.

- The fundamental principles of feng shui are known as *san cao*, or the three treasures, known as heaven, earth, and man. Chinese culture believes that man is the nexus—the connection—between heaven and earth.
    - Heaven represents your mind and body genetics. According to feng shui theory, it comes from the heavens and can't be changed.

    - Earth represents the environmental influences that affect your everyday life.

    - Man represents the good deeds you do unto others, your level of self-development, and other studies as well as your thought patterns (i.e., positive versus negative thoughts).

The Five Elements Theory

- From the most ancient times, Chinese culture has imagined that the world is made up of five basic elements: wood, water, fire, earth, and metal. The techniques of traditional Chinese medicine utilize the five elements theory.

- In fact, the flow of qi is actually mapped according to when each element is most influential in the human body. These five elements combine in different ways to make the things we see in nature, including people. The five elements are also part of the philosophy of tai chi and tai chi chuan.

- The five elements are an expansion of the theory of yin and yang. In the *I Jing*, creation is described in the following way: "In the beginning there was the One (the Wuji). The One gave birth to the Two (Yin and Yang). The Two gave birth to the Three (Yin, Yang plus one more), and the Three gave birth to the Five (the Five Elements)."

- The five elements are the basic building blocks of the material world—fire, wood, water, earth, and metal. Certainly, they were conceived of because ancient Chinese philosophers could see them physically present in the world, and they seemed to be the quintessence of other things. Water, for example, was the essence of all things liquid, like blood, honey, or wine. And it seemed clear that these elements could combine together to make other things in the material world, the most complex of these being a human.

- But the five elements are also expressions of qi energy. They describe a certain state or vibration of qi that can also be seen in the world. Wood, for example, represents the energy of growth and expansion. Water, obviously, is associated with the energy of flow and movement. The five elements, therefore, are associated with many other references.

- For example, fire is associated with the season of summer, the sun, the color red, and the human organ of the heart. Wood is associated with the spring, the organ of the liver, the emotion of anger and frustration, and the color green. Metal is the autumn, the organ of the lungs, the emotion of sadness and melancholy (depression), and the color white or silver.

- The five elements both create and destroy each other. Part of the theory of the five elements is a model of a continuous pattern of genesis that goes as follows: Water creates wood, wood creates fire, fire creates earth, earth creates metal, and metal creates water.

- In the same way, there is a pattern of destruction, or dissolution, that goes as follows: Fire destroys metal, metal destroys wood, wood destroys earth, earth destroys water, and water destroys fire.

- When you notice that your life is out of balance—and your body will tell you with pain, injuries, or illnesses—you might go to a traditional Chinese physician. The physician will diagnose you and typically report that one or more of your elements are out of balance and that you need a treatment that will balance them.

- From the doctor, then, you next might go visit your qigong master to get a specific qigong exercise for that condition. The condition is often associated with a season, because each element is connected to a season. An example is the spring, or wood element, causing liver disruption.

Suggested Reading

Bond, *The First 16 Secrets of Chi*.

Lebeau and Raytis, *Feng Shui Your Mind*.

Activities

1. Take a look at your bedroom. Imagine that you were a breeze or a stream of water (the elements that flow). Would you be able to move freely through the room and out the door? Or would you get stuck behind

furniture, or a pile of clothes? Then, take a similar look at your house as a whole. Finally, take a look at your office work space.

2. Every day, we're presented with dozens of opportunities to make choices. Try recording one day's worth of choice points and then making a note of whether the eventual choice (and its execution) was effortless or challenging. In other words, did it flow?

Taking Practice Deeper
Lecture 23

Tai chi has a universe of material to dive into, to explore, to learn about. In fact, in the 24-movement routine that you have been learning, you have been presented with some of the basics of the steps, the hands, and the transitions that move together, but there is still much more to learn about them. In this lecture, you will investigate some intermediate material from each of the movements in the 24-movement form. If you don't feel like you're ready for more advanced or intermediate movements, let this lecture plant a seed in your mind, and you can come back to it later.

Movements Included in This Lecture
- Opening the door

- Parting the wild horse's mane

- Crane spreads wings

- Playing the *pei pa*

- Repulsing monkey

- Grasping the bird's tail

- Wave hands like clouds

- High pat on horse

- Snake creeps down

High pat on horse.

Snake creeps down.

Suggested Reading

Liang, *Simplified Tai Chi Chuan*.

Ross, *The Tai Chi Companion*.

Activities

1. Inside *The Tai Chi Companion* is an outline for how to keep a practice journal. Start a journal, and each time you practice, write down your performance notes.

2. Practice "four corners tai chi": Perform your 24-movement routine four times back to back, each time commencing facing a different direction.

The Evolution of Tai Chi
Lecture 24

In this final lecture, you will learn how tai chi is adapting to the 21st century. What is the value of martial arts in the contemporary world? How worthwhile is a form of medicine based on energy and movement in a world of science, drugs, and surgery? Now that you have completed this 24-lecture series, you can consider yourself to be part of the movement to bring tai chi and qigong into the mainstream of Western culture.

The Evolution of Tai Chi

- Tai chi and qigong have come a long way since Hua Tuo went out into the countryside to investigate a plague and ended up inventing the dance of the five animals. And you no longer have to be part of a particular clan to learn the techniques of a formal style. Today, advanced lessons on almost every style are as close as your laptop. Just go to YouTube, and you can find thousands of clips.

- But the availability of tai chi chuan and qigong instruction is only a part of the puzzle. We live in a world of increasing imbalances. The faster pace of modern life—brought about by our wonderful advances in science and technology—also brings with it greater levels of stress and further disconnections from other people and from nature. The fundamental essence of tai chi—the importance of harmony and balance—can be lost.

- What are the ways that these practices are evolving? One of the most interesting new things is how tai chi teachers are using technology to share or showcase their art.

- Many teachers are also using video to record their students' performances for evaluation, the same way Olympic trainers and professional football coaches do. In fact, video is the new medium of tai chi chuan and qigong.

- A quick search on YouTube will turn up thousands of tai chi–related videos, of all styles and aspects. Have you ever wondered what tai chi in Istanbul looks like? You can find it on YouTube. And, of course, as more and more people communicate, study, and do business on mobile devices like tablets and smartphones, tai chi chuan and qigong mobile apps have started to multiply.

- Hand in hand with the use of new technology to share and showcase tai chi practices is the evolution of the very way it is taught. By its nature, tai chi chuan and qigong are typically taught by relatively traditional methods—from master to student, passing along skills and secrets according to merit and dedication.

- There is an old Chinese saying in martial arts: *Shr tu ru fudz*, which translates as, "A teacher and his student are like father and son." Many traditionalists lament that in these modern times, students can pay for lessons and essentially "buy" new routines to learn or sparring tricks to employ.

- Nevertheless, the people who love these ancient practices are starting to loosen up a bit, following the trends of how people in the 21st century get connected and share information. One popular way that tai chi players get together is in meet-up groups. These informal and noncommercial gatherings can be found all over the world, and they are a way that tai chi people can meet, practice forms together, and especially find push hands partners.

- Social networking websites, such as Facebook and LinkedIn, each have dozens of very active tai chi chuan and qigong groups. Some of these groups have more than 1,000 members, and the conversations that take place online (about technique, history, and philosophy) are extremely lively.

- Another very interesting aspect of how tai chi is following new trends is how the competitive aspects are being brought into focus. There is a trend called "gamification," an attempt to attract younger people to try tai chi.

- One of the early advocates of the power of tai chi to change one's life is Al Huang, a nontraditional teacher of tai chi who has been a mainstay at the Esalen Institute in Big Sur, California, for more than 40 years. Early in his career, he was an assistant to Alan Watts. Now, he has traveled the world teaching a version of tai chi based on his understanding of Chinese calligraphy and the five elements.

- One of the themes that runs through the work of the modern tai chi teachers is that tai chi was traditionally presented to beginners in a way that makes it difficult to learn. Traditional tai chi chuan and qigong can be extremely complex, and teachers often focus on precision and detail in a way that quickly pushes newcomers away.

- Roger Jahnke is the founder of Tai Chi Easy, a program whose name says it all. Jahnke is a well-respected qigong master and tai chi chuan teacher who has also been a part of the effort to formally research the medical benefits of tai chi and qigong. He has worked with a number of top-notch universities and research institutions and is often a keynote speaker for medical conferences. He is also one of the founders of the National Qigong Association.

The Future of Tai Chi

- Tai chi practices—tai chi chuan, qigong, and philosophy—are definitely changing to keep up with the times. But a real evolution is a transformation, a thing changing its nature, that includes its past but transcends it to reach into places it could not go before. So, where can tai chi go in the future?

- It is possible that it will emerge as a serious solution to the main challenges, or imbalances, of modern society. It will become familiar, not foreign—mainstream, not niche. It is possible that there will be a time in the not-to-distant future when tai chi practice is a fundamental part of the fabric of modern Western society, in schools, hospitals, workplaces, public places, sports, entertainment, and art.

Joining a tai chi group can help you experience a sense of community while engaging in tai chi practice.

- Tai chi will learn to speak the language of younger generations and may in fact be a bridge between the generations, as both young people and old meet in a common space to play tai chi together.

- The philosophy of balance and harmony is universally embraced by just about every religion and culture, but modern tai chi can give it a language and a structure for learning, and then perhaps it will provide a guideline for science, education, politics, and governance. These are some of the things that are possible as tai chi evolves into the modern world of the future.

- But in the midst of all that, remember to have fun. Enjoy the journey of tai chi, a never-ending path toward harmony. That's why the ancient masters reminded us continuously that tai chi was meant to be played—not worked.

Suggested Reading

Huang, *Embrace Tiger, Return to Mountain*.

Read, *The Manual of Bean Curd Boxing*.

Activities

1. Go online to www.meetup.com. This website helps people with shared interests find each other and connect. The gatherings are mostly informal and free. Check to see if there are any tai chi groups meeting in your area.

2. Do you want David-Dorian Ross to give you a personal tip for your tai chi practice? Upload a short sample of your 24-movement form, and he will send you a response. Contact him at daviddorianross.com.

Bibliography

Bond, Luk Chun. *The First 16 Secrets of Chi: Feng Shui for the Human Body*. Berkeley: Frog Books, 2002. An unusual form of tai chi—but the author tries to show how practicing tai chi chuan is like doing feng shui for your body.

Buck, Pearl S. *All Men Are Brothers*. Heritage Press, 1948. *The Water Margin* is one of the most loved examples of classical Chinese literature. It is a classic, moreover, in the wuxia tradition—108 martial heroes fighting against corruption and tyranny. In 1933, Pearl S. Buck translated this massive novel into English with the title *All Men Are Brothers*.

Chia, Mantak. *Healing Light of the Tao: Foundational Practices to Awaken Chi Energy*. Rochester: Destiny Books, 1993. An easy-to-read-and-apply introduction to the microcosmic orbit.

Chinese Health Qigong Association. *Wu Qin Xi: Five-Animal Qigong Exercises*. London: Singing Dragon, 2008. This book is an official publication from China, complete with photo illustrations for all the exercises. Contains both the A and B exercises for each of the five animals.

Chuckrow, Robert. *Tai Chi Dynamics: Principles of Natural Movement, Health & Self-Development*. Wolfeboro: YMAA Publication Center, 2008. The author uses extensive examples from common, everyday movements to illustrate the fundamental principles of tai chi.

Cohen, Ken. *The Way of Qigong: The Art and Science of Chinese Energy Healing*. New York: Ballantine Books, 1997. Ken Cohen is one of the treasures of tai chi in America. He is a scholar of qigong, is fluent in multiple dialects of Chinese, and is an accomplished master of both tai chi and qigong.

Cohen, Mark. *Inside Zhang Zhuan*. Hawaii: Mark Cohen, 2012. It may be hard to imagine an entire book (300-plus pages, no less!) on "standing like a tree"—but the author manages to make it both informative and practical. Includes lots of photos and illustrations.

Crompton, Paul. *Tai Chi Combat*. Boston: Shambhala, 1990. Lots of photo illustrations in this book. The author shows both self-defense applications and use of the movements for the push hands game.

Dreyer, Danny, and Katherine Dreyer. *ChiRunning: A Revolutionary Approach to Effortless, Injury-Free Running*. New York: Fireside, 2004. This is a really inventive use of tai chi. Thousands of people who like running have found a way to do it more safely, effectively, and enjoyably through ChiRunning.

Frantzis, Bruce. *Opening the Energy Gates of Your Body: Qigong for Lifelong Health*. Berkeley: North Atlantic Books, 1993. Bruce Frantzis studied in China for more than a decade before returning to the United States to share his qigong and tai chi discoveries with the West.

Huang, Al Chung-liang. *Embrace Tiger, Return to Mountain*. London: Singing Dragon, 2011. This is a favorite among students beginning to study tai chi. Al Huang is a role model for how to play tai chi chuan and qigong—with joy, personal style, and wild abandon!

Huang, Al Chung-liang, and Jerry Lynch. *Thinking Body, Dancing Mind: Taosports for Extraordinary Performance in Athletics, Business, and Life*. New York: Bantam Books, 1992. This is a great book on applying the experiences of tai chi in business as well as the rest of life.

Jahnke, Roger. *The Healing Promise of Qi: Creating Extraordinary Wellness through Qigong and Tai Chi*. New York: Contemporary Books, 2002. The author makes understanding the theory and practice qigong very accessible. Roger Jahnke is a tireless promoter of the benefits of internal medicine.

Kaye, Les. *Zen at Work*. New York: Random House, 1996. The author relates his personal experiences of bringing some spirituality and philosophy to his office.

Kuo, Lien-ying. *Tai Chi Chuan in Theory and Practice*. Berkeley: Blue Snake Books, 1999. Lien-ying Kuo is one of the most authentic and original tai chi masters to arrive early in the United States from China. This book is his transmission of very old-school tai chi lessons.

Lebeau, Jill, and Maureen Raytis. *Feng Shui Your Mind: Four Easy Steps to Rapidly Transform Your Life*. Indianapolis: Blue Dog Publishing, 2010. This book is divided into four sections, entitled "Declutter," "Envision," "Position," and "Attract." It's a hip and very practical guide to actions that use the science of feng shui to make adjustments in your own mindset that will change the energy flow of your life.

Leonard, George. *Mastery: The Keys to Success and Long-Term Fulfillment*. New York: Penguin, 1992. Mastery is a process rather than a final state to achieve—and in this book, the author shows us how we can master life as much as any sport or business goal.

———. *The Way of Aikido: Life Lessons from an American Sensei*. New York: Penguin, 2000. Tai chi chuan from China and aikido from Japan are close cousins. Both are martial arts based on the concept that softness overcomes hardness—and both are arts that can apply their principles to everyday life. This is a wonderful book by the man who coined the phrase "the human potential movement."

Liang, Shou-yu. *Simplified Tai Chi Chuan: 24 Postures with Applications & Standard 48 Postures*. Wolfeboro: YMAA Publication, 2014. You get a two-for-one bonus in this book: both the 24-movement form and the 48-movement form. Each routine is broken down and illustrated step by step and includes the practical self-defense application of each move.

Lo, Ben, and Martin Inn, trans. *The Essence of Tai Chi Chuan: The Literary Tradition*. Berkeley: North Atlantic Books, 1979. This is a clear and easy-to-read translation that invites the reader to think like a tai chi player.

Lu-tang, Sun. *A Study of Taijiquan*. Translated by Tim Cartmell. Berkeley: North Atlantic Books, 2003. Sun Lu-tang was the creator of Sun-style tai chi, and one of the reasons he is held in high esteem is because of the books he wrote on tai chi, *xing-yi*, and *bagua*—the trinity of "internal" martial arts. He was also one of the first to make extensive use of photo illustrations. Cartmell provides a great translation of Sun's famous book on tai chi.

Man-ch'ing, Cheng, Benjamin Pang Jeng Lo, and Martin Inn. *Cheng Tzu's Thirteen Treatises on T'ai Chi Ch'uan.* Berkeley: North Atlantic Books, 1985. Cheng Man-ch'ing was a disciple and personal physician to Yang Chen-fu, grandson of the creator of the Yang style of tai chi. He was also a "master of the five excellences": poetry, calligraphy, painting, Chinese medicine, and tai chi chuan.

Newmark, Amy, and Angela Timashenka Geiger. *Chicken Soup for the Soul: Living with Alzheimer's & Other Dementias: 101 Stories of Caregiving, Coping, and Compassion.* Cos Cob, CT: Chicken Soup for the Soul Publishing, 2014. I The *Chicken Soup* stories and lessons mirror the message of tai chi.

Olson, Stuart Alve. *Tai Chi: Sensing Hands.* Unique Publications, 1999. Stuart Olson was the disciple of the great tai chi master T. T. Liang and has written many books about his teacher's philosophy and technique. This is an interesting translation of *tui shou*; instead of "pushing hands," Olson translates it as "sensing hands." In this book, the author leads us through the techniques of the second pillar in the light of developing sensitivity and insight into connecting to others.

———. *Tai Chi Sword, Sabre & Staff.* Bubbling Well Press, 1986. This serves as a very nice introduction to the main weapons associated with tai chi practice.

Olson, Stuart Alve, and Patrick Gross. *Tai Ji Quan Treatise: Attributed to the Song Dynasty Daoist Priest Zhang Sanfeng.* Phoenix, AZ: Valley Spirit Arts, 2011. Although Zhang San-feng is thought by most authorities to be only a myth, the stories and writings attributed to him contain the foundation of all tai chi chuan theory and practice. Stuart Olson applies his considerable knowledge of tai chi to the commentary and analysis of the book said to be written by Zhang San-feng.

Read, Paul. *The Manual of Bean Curd Boxing: Tai Chi and the Noble Art of Leaving Things Undone*. Granada: Lulu Press, 2012. Read's lighthearted—but sharp-witted—writing style softly guides you to looking at all of life from the perspective of softness and effortlessness.

Rosenfeld, Arthur. *Tai Chi—The Perfect Exercise: Finding Health, Happiness, Balance and Strength*. Boston, MA: Da Capo Press, 2013. This book offers a deep discussion of how the philosophy of yin-yang balance brings inner peace. The author draws together many elements of both Eastern and Western culture to explain tai chi philosophy.

Ross, David-Dorian. *Exercising the Soul*. MLF Press, 2012. This book will help you get started in tai chi, especially if you are wondering what to expect when you start studying.

————. *Power, Freedom and Flow: Your Journey to Health and Happiness*. Los Gatos, CA: The Wellness Evolution Press, 2003. In this book, you will find an even further discussion on the principles of synergy and flow.

————. *The Tai Chi Companion*. 1994. This is a workbook, covering all 24 movements of the short form taught in this course. Multiple illustrations guide you through every movement. As a bonus, the workbook also teaches you the basic principles of forms practice.

Sarno, John. *Healing Back Pain: The Mind-Body Connection*. New York: Warner Books, 1991. This is a classic reference guide to healing chronic low back pain. The author is a pioneer in looking at the cause of back pain as a mind-body disconnect.

Sim, Davidine, and David Gaffney. *Chen Style Taijiquan: The Source of Taiji Boxing*. Berkeley: Blue Snake Books, 2002. These authors are "indoor" students of the Chen family and have traveled regularly to Chen village in China. They have heard the stories of origins of tai chi chuan from the horse's mouth.

Slingerland, Edward. *Trying Not to Try: The Art and Science of Spontaneity*. New York: Crown Publishers, 2014. The author draws from the ancient Chinese concept of wu wei and shows how that can benefit contemporary life.

Tsung-hwa, Jou. *The Tao of Tai Chi Chuan*. North Clarendon: Tuttle Publishing, 1989. This is a great introduction to many different aspects of tai chi, including philosophy, history, and illustrated instructions. But the best part is the stories that are included—particularly about Zhang San-feng, the legendary inventor of tai chi.

U.S. Department of Health and Human Services, et al. *Physical Activity and Health: A Report of the Surgeon General*. Washington, DC: U.S. Superintendent of Documents, 1998. In 1996, the surgeon general released this report, which shows that fewer than 15 percent of the adults in America get the minimum recommended amount of daily physical activity to stay alive. Inactivity can be equivalent to smoking two packs of cigarettes every day. A little tai chi could go a long way toward extending the lifespan of someone you know.

Waitzkin, Josh. *The Art of Learning: An Inner Journey to Optimal Performance*. New York: Free Press, 2007. Josh Waitzkin started out in early life as an international chess prodigy; you may remember his story from the movie *Chasing Bobby Fisher*. As he grew older, he wanted to take on another challenge and began to study tai chi—particularly competitive push hands. This is a fascinating account of an American who went on to win the gold medal in Taiwan at the world championships.

Wayne, Peter. *The Harvard Medical School Guide to Tai Chi*. Boston and London: Shambhala, 2012. This is perhaps the most influential recent book on tai chi, from a respected authority in medicine. It is a generalized report on much of the recent research into the health benefits of tai chi.

Wollering, Loretta. *Anatomy of Fitness: Tai Chi*. Hinkler Books, 2014. This is a new book by a longtime disciple of the late Master Jou Tsung-hwa. The *Anatomy of Fitness* series has covered other disciplines (such as hatha yoga and Pilates, for example) to show exactly how the movements engage the bones, muscles, and nervous system.

Bibliography

Yang, Jwing-ming. *Eight Simple Qigong Exercises for Health.* Wolfeboro: YMAA Publications, 1997. Dr. Yang is one of the most prolific authors on the topics of qigong and tai chi chuan. This book contains movement-by-movement instruction as well as photo illustrations.

———. *Tai Chi Chuan Martial Applications: Advanced Yang Style Tai Chi Chuan.* Wolfeboro: YMAA Publications, 1996. In this book, Dr. Yang demonstrates his roots as a serious martial artist when he was a young man in China. He shows the fighting application (no holds barred) of essential tai chi techniques and also introduces the reader to a "fighting set," a routine made for two people to practice the self-defense techniques of tai chi with a partner.

———. *Tai Chi Secrets of the Wu Style: Chinese Classics, Translations, Commentary.* Wolfeboro: YMAA Publications, 2002. This is one of the only books available in English with a translation of some of the early Chinese writings on Wu style. The author explains in very technical style the unique features of Wu-style tai chi and why it is so important in understanding the history of tai chi as a whole.

———. *Taiji Sword, Classical Yang Style: The Complete Form, Qigong & Applications.* Wolfeboro: YMAA Publications, 2010. This sword routine is even longer than the form demonstrated in this course. As an added bonus, the author includes qigong exercises to go along with the sword practice.

Notes

Notes

Notes

Notes

Notes